A NEW SYSTEM OF CHEMICAL PHILOSOPHY

THE SCIENCE CLASSICS LIBRARY

General Editors:
DAGOBERT D. RUNES
THOMAS KIERNAN

John Dalton

A New System of Chemical Philosophy

INTRODUCTION BY ALEXANDER JOSEPH
*Director, National Science Foundation In-Service
Institute in Physics, Bronx Community College—
City College, City University of New York*

New York: THE CITADEL PRESS

FIRST PAPERBOUND EDITION, 1964
The Citadel Press
222 Park Avenue South
New York 3, N.Y.

INTRODUCTION

1766

    John Dalton, English chemist and physicist, was born on September 6, 1776, at Eaglesfield in England. He was educated by his father, who was head of the Quaker School at Eaglesfield. When his father retired, John Dalton replaced him as head of the school. Subsequently, he taught at various other schools and in 1785 became joint manager of a school in Kendall. Later, he was appointed a teacher of natural philosophy and mathematics at the New College in Manchester. Then he went to Manchester College, Oxford, and when that college moved back to Manchester, he returned with it. In 1794 he was elected a member of the Manchester Literary and Philosophical Society, where he presented his first scientific paper, "Extraordinary Facts Relating to the Vision of Colours." In 1803 he wrote a paper, "Absorption of Gases by Water and Other Liquids," which involved his law of partial pressures. This same law was discovered simultaneously by Gay-Lussac, with whom it is usually associated.

    Dalton helped put chemistry on a firm theoretical foundation. He was in a direct line of scientific descendants from Black through Cavendish and Lavoisier to Proust, who started the chemical revolution at the end of the eighteenth century.

    However, it is in his work in atomic theory that Dalton made his most important contributions.

    He returned to the older Greek theory of Democritus —that all things are basically made up of tiny particles which cannot be further subdivided. Dalton visualized atoms as solid particles. He naturally was not able to predict the splitting of the atom. As he once stated in his work, "all bodies of sensible magnitude, whether liquid or solid, are constituted by a vast number of extremely small particles or atoms of matter bound together by a force of attraction which is more or less powerful according to the circumstance." Here we see the beginnings of valence bonds. From this concept came the idea of atomic weight. Dalton did not foresee the existences of isotopes of the same atom, with different atomic weights: and, in fact, it was not until 1912 that atomic isotopes were first established experimentally.

Dalton's work on atomic weights led him to the formulation of the first atomic chart. This of course eventually led to Mendelyeev's Periodic Chart of the then known elements, during the year 1867.

Dalton's ideas first appeared on page 248 of his notebook, covering the years 1802-1804. Here one can find the first mention of atomic weights. His Atomic Theory first appeared in print in a book by Thomas Thomson, "System of Chemistry." Dalton was honored in being asked to give a series of lectures at the Royal Institution and was elected a fellow of the Royal Society in 1822. In 1830 he was elected a foreign associate in the French Academy of Science.

Dalton applied the term "complex atoms" to the product of the reaction between two elements, which today we call a compound. The other major discrepancy between his theories and modern chemistry was his use of the weight of hydrogen, a relative weight of one, as the basic unit in measuring and expressing atomic weight; 16 for oxygen is now commonly used. However, from the viewpoint of modern physics, the proton or hydrogen nucleus, with an atomic mass of one, is used as the basic building block.

During the course of his lifetime he maintained daily weather observations, so that his records contained 200,000 observations. Unfortunately, most of the Dalton relics and papers were destroyed during the air-raid at Manchester during World War II.

This is the first and basic volume of his work. In a sense, the publication of the first volume of *A New System of Chemical Philosophy* in 1808 started the chemical revolution of the nineteenth century, and Dalton's chemical philosophy foretold most of the advances in chemistry made during the nineteenth century.

A. J.

CONTENTS

PREFACE

It was the author's intention when this work was put to press to publish it entire in one volume; but he is now induced to publish it in two parts, for reasons which it may be proper to announce.

Various essays of his were read before the Literary and Philosophical Society of Manchester, chiefly on heat and elastic fluids, and were published in the 5th Volume of their Memoirs, in 1802. The new views which these essays developed, were considered both curious and important. The essays were republished in several Philosophical Journals, and soon after translated into French and German, and circulated abroad through the medium of the foreign Journals. The author was not remiss in prosecuting his researches, in which he was considerably assisted by the application of principles derived from the above essays. In 1803, he was gradually led to those primary Laws, which seem to obtain in regard to heat, and to chemical combinations, and which it is the object of the present work to exhibit and elucidate. A brief outline of them was first publicly given the ensuing winter in a course of Lectures on Natural Philosophy, at the Royal Institution in London, and was left for publication in the Journals of the Institution; but he is not informed whether that was done. The author has ever since been occasionally urged by several of his philosophical friends to lose no time in communicating the results of his inquiries to the public, alleging, that the interests of science, and his own reputation, might suffer by delay. In the spring of 1807, he was induced to offer the exposition of the principles herein contained in a course of Lectures, which were twice read in Edinburgh, and once in Glasgow. On these occasions he was honoured with the attention of gentlemen, universally acknowledged to be of the first respectability for their scientific attainments: most of whom were pleased to express their desire to see the publication of the doctrine in the present form, as soon as convenient. Upon the author's return to Manchester he began to prepare for the press. Several experiments required to be repeated; other new ones were to be made; almost the whole system both in matter and manner was to be new, and consequently required more time for the composition and arrangement. These considerations, together with the daily avocations of profession, have delayed the work nearly a year; and, judging from the past, it may require another year before it can be completed. In the mean time, as the doctrine of heat, and the general principles of Chemical Synthesis, are in a good degree independent of the future details, there can no great detriment arise to the author, or inconvenience to his readers, in submitting what is already prepared, to the inspection of the public.

MAY, 1808.

A NEW SYSTEM OF CHEMICAL PHILOSOPHY

CHAPTER I

ON HEAT OR CALORIC

The most probable opinion concerning the nature of caloric is, that of its being an elastic fluid of great subtilty, the particles of which repel one another, but are attracted by all other bodies.

When all surrounding bodies are of one temperature, then the heat attached to them is in a quiescent state; the absolute quantities of heat in any two bodies in this case are not equal, whether we take the bodies of equal weights or of equal bulks. Each kind of matter has its peculiar affinity for heat, by which it requires a certain portion of the fluid, in order to be in equilibrium with other bodies at a certain temperature. Were the *whole quantities* of heat in bodies of equal weight or bulk, or even the *relative quantities,* accurately ascertained, for any temperature, the numbers expressing those quantities would constitute a table of *specific heats,* analogous to a table of *specific gravities,* and would be an important acquisition to science. Attempts of this kind have been made with very considerable success.

Whether the specific heats, could they be thus obtained for one temperature, would express the relation at every other temperature, while the bodies retained their form, is an inquiry of some moment. From the experiments hitherto made there seems little doubt of its being nearly so; but it is perhaps more correct to deduce the specific heat of bodies from equal *bulks* than from equal *weights*. It is very certain that the two methods will not give precisely the same results, because the expansions of different bodies by equal increments of temperature are not the same. But before this subject can well be considered, we should first settle what is intended to be meant by the word temperature.

On Temperature

And the Instruments for measuring it

The notion of the specific heat of bodies and of temperature, may be well conceived from a system of cylindrical vessels of different diameters connected with each other by pipes at the bottom, and a small cylindrical tube attached to the system, all capable of holding water or any other liquid, and placed perpendicular to the horizon. (See Plate 1. Fig. 1.) The cylinders are to represent the different specific heats of bodies; and the small tube, being divided into equal parts, is to represent the thermometer or measure of temperature. If water be poured into one vessel it rises to the same level in them all, and in the thermometer; if equal portions be successively poured in, there will be equal rises in the vessels and in the tube; the water is obviously intended to represent heat or caloric. According to this notion, then, it is evident that equal increments of heat in any body correspond to equal increments of temperature.

3

This view of the subject necessarily requires, that if two bodies be taken of any one temperature, and then be raised to any other temperature, the additional quantities of heat received by each will be exactly proportioned to the whole qualities of that fluid previously contained in them. This conclusion, though it may be nearly consistent with facts in general, is certainly not strictly true. For, in elastic fluids, it is well known, an increase of *bulk* occasions an increase of specific heat, though the weight and temperature continue the same. It is probable then that solids and liquids too, as they increase in bulk by heat, increase in their capacity or capability of receiving more. This circumstance, however, might not affect the conclusion above, provided all bodies increased in one and the same proportion by heat; but as this is not the case, the objection to the conclusion appears of validity. Suppose it were allowed that a thermometer ought to indicate the accession of *equal* increments of the fluid denominated caloric, to the body of which it was to show the temperature;—suppose too that a measure of air or elastic fluid was to be the body; query, whether ought the air to be suffered to expand by the temperature, or to be confined to the same space of one measure? It appears to me the most likely in theory to procure a standard capacity for heat by subjecting a body to heat, *while its bulk is kept constantly the same.* Let $m =$ the quantity of heat necessary to raise the elastic fluid 10° in temperature in this case; then $m + d =$ the quantity necessary to raise the same 10°, when suffered to expand, d being the difference of the absolute quantities of heat contained by the body in the two cases. Now, $^1/_{10}\ m =$ the quantity of heat necessary to raise the temperature 1° in the first case; but $^1/_{10}\ (m + d)$ cannot be the quantity necessary in the second case; it will be a less quantity in the lower degrees, and a greater in the higher.

If these principles be admitted, they may be applied to liquids and solids; a liquid, as water, cannot be raised in temperature equally by equal increments of heat, unless it is confined within the same space by an extraordinary and perhaps incalculable force; if we suffer it to take its ordinary course of expansion, then not equal, but increasing increments of heat will raise its temperature uniformly. If sufficient force were applied to condense a liquid or solid, there can be no doubt but heat would be given out, as with elastic fluids.

It may perhaps be urged by some that the difference of heat in condensed and rarefied air, and by analogy probably in the supposed cases of liquids and solids, is too small to have sensible influence on the capacities or affinities of bodies for heat; that the effects are such, as only to raise or depress the temperature a few degrees; when perhaps the whole mass of heat is equivalent to two or three thousand such degrees; and that a volume of air supposed to contain 2005° of temperature being rarefied till it become 2000°, or lost 5° of temperature, may still be considered as having its capacity invariable. This may be granted if the data are admissible; but the true changes of temperature consequent to the condensation and rarefaction of air have never been determined. I have shown (Manchester Mem. Vol. 5, Pt. 2.) that in the process of admitting air into a vacuum, and of liberating condensed air, the enclosed thermometer is affected as if in a medium of 50° higher or lower temperature; but the effects of instantaneously doubling the density of air, or replenishing a vacuum, cannot easily be derived from those or any other facts I am acquainted with; they may perhaps raise the temperature one hundred degrees or more. The great heat produced in charging an air-gun is a proof of a great change of capacity in the enclosed air. Upon the whole then it may be concluded, that the change of bulk in the same body by change of temperature, is productive of considerable effect on its capacity for heat, but that we are not yet in possession of data to determine its effect on elastic fluids, and still less on liquids and solids. M. De Luc found, that in mixing *equal weights* of water at the freezing and boiling temperature, 32° and 212°, the mixture indicated nearly 119° of Fahrenheit's mercurial thermometer; but the numberical mean is 122°; if he had mixed *equal bulks* of water at 32° and 212°, he would have found a mean of 115°. Now the means determined by experiment in both these ways are probably too high; for, water of these two temperatures being mixed, loses about 1-90th of its bulk; this condensation of volume (whether arising from an increased affinity of aggregation, or the effect of external mechanical compression, is all one) must expel a quantity of heat, and raise the temperature above the true mean. It is not improbable that the true mean temperature between 32° and 212° may be as low as 110° of Fahrenheit.

It has been generally admitted that if two portions of any liquid, of equal weight but of different temperatures, be mixed together, the mixture must indicate the true mean temperature; and that instrument which corresponds with it is an accurate measure of temperature. But if the preceding observations be correct, it may be questioned whether any two liquids will agree in giving the same mean temperature upon being mixed as above.

In the present imperfect mode of estimating temperature, the equable expansion of mercury is adopted as a scale for its measure. This cannot be correct for two reasons; lst. the mixture of water of different temperatures is always *below* the mean by the mercurial thermometer, for instance, water of 32° and 212° being mixed, gives 119° by the thermometer; whereas it appears from the preceding remarks, that the temperature of such mixture ought to be found above the mean 122°; 2d. mercury appears by the most recent experiments to expand by the same law as water; namely, as the square of the temperature from the point of greatest density. The apparently equal expansion of mercury arises from our taking a small portion of the scale of expansion, and that at some distance from the freezing point of the liquid.

From what has been remarked it appears that we have not yet any mode easily practicable for ascertaining what is the true mean between any two temperatures, as those of freezing and boiling water; nor any thermometer which can be considered as approximating nearly to accuracy.

Heat is a very important agent in nature; it cannot be doubted that so active a principle must be subject to general laws. If the phenomena indicate otherwise, it is because we do not take a sufficiently comprehensive view of them. Philosophers have sought, but in vain, for a body that should expand uniformly, or in arithmetical progression, by equal increments of heat; liquids have been tried, and found to expand unequally, all of them expanding more in the higher temperatures than in the lower, but no two exactly alike. Mercury has appeared to have the least variation, or approach nearest to uniform expansion, and on that and other accounts has been generally preferred in the construction of thermometers. Water has been rejected, as the most unequally expanding liquid yet known. Since the publication of my experiments on the expansion of elastic fluids by heat, and those of Gay Lussac, immediately succeeding them, both demonstrating the perfect sameness in all permanently elastic fluids in this respect; it has been imagined by some that gases expand equally; but this is not corroborated by experience from other sources.-

Some time ago it occurred to me as probable, that

water and mercury, notwithstanding their apparent diversity, actually expand by the same law, and that the quantity of expansion is as the square of the temperature from
their respective freezing points. Water very nearly accords
with this law according to the present scale of temperature,
and the little deviation observable is exactly of the sort
that ought to exist, from the known error of the equal
division of the mercurial scale. By prosecuting this inquiry
I found that the mercurial and water scales divided according to the principle just mentioned, would perfectly
accord, as far as they were comparable; and that the law
will probably extend to all other pure liquids; but not to
heterogeneous compounds, as liquid solutions of salts.

If the law of the expansion of liquids be such as just
mentioned, it is natural to expect that other phenomena of
heat will be characteristic of the same law. It may be seen
in my Essay on the Force of Steam that the elastic force or
tension of steam in contact with water, increases *nearly* in
a geometrical progression to equal increments of temperature, *as measured by the common mercurial scale*; it was
not a little surprising to me at the time to find such an
approach to a regular progression, and I was then inclined
to think, that the want of perfect coincidence was owing to
inaccuracy in the division of the received thermometer;
but overawed by the authority of Crawford, who seemed to
have proved past doubt that the error of the thermometer
no where amounted to more than one or two degrees, I
durst not venture to throw out more than a suspicion at
the conclusion of the essay, on the expansion of elastic
fluids by heat, that the error was probably 3 or 4°, as De
Luc had determined; to admit of an error in the supposed
mean, amounting to 12°, seemed unwarrantable. However
it now appears that the force of steam in contact with
water, increases *accurately* in geometrical progression to

equal increments of temperature, provided those increments are measured by a thermometer of water or mercury, the scales of which are divided according to the above-
mentioned law.

The Force of Steam having been found to vary by the
above law, it was natural to expect that of air to do the
same; for, air (meaning any permanently elastic fluid) and
steam are essentially the same, differing only in certain
modifications. Accordingly it was found upon trial that air
expands in geometrical progression to equal increments of
temperature, measured as above. Steam detached from
water, by which it is rendered incapable of increase or
diminution in quantity, was found by Gay Lussac, to have
the same quantity of expansion as the permanently elastic
fluids. I had formerly conjectured that air expands as the
cube of the temperature from absolute privation, as hinted
in the essay above-mentioned; but I am now obliged to
abandon that conjecture.

The union of so many analogies in favor the preceding hypothesis of temperature is almost sufficient to establish it; but one remarkable trait of temperature derived
from experiments on the heating and cooling of bodies,
which does not accord with the received scale, and which,
nevertheless, claims special consideration, is, that *a body in
cooling loses heat in proportion to its excess of temperature above that of the cooling medium*; or that the
temperature descends in geometrical progression in equal
moments of time. Thus if a body were 1000° above the
medium; the times in cooling from 1000° to 100, from 100
to 10, and from 10 to 1°, ought all to be the same. This,
though nearly, is not accurately true, if we adopt the
common scale, as is well known; the times in the lower
intervals of temperature are found longer than in the
upper; but the new scale proposed, by shortening the

lower degrees, and lengthening the higher, is found perfectly according to this remarkable law of heat.

Temperature then will be found to have four most
remarkable analogies to support it.

1. All pure homogenous liquids, as water and mercury, expand from the point of their congelation, or greatest density, a quantity always as the square of the temperature from that point.

2. The force of steam from pure liquids, as water,
ether, etc. constitutes a geometrical progression to increments of temperature in arithmetical progression.

3. The expansion of permanent elastic fluids is in
geometrical progression to equal increments of temperature.

4. The refrigeration of bodies is in geometrical progression in equal increments of time.

A mercurial thermometer graduated according to this
principle will differ from the ordinary one with equidiffer-
ential scale, by having its lower degrees smaller and the
upper ones larger; the mean between freezing and boiling
water, or 122° on the new scale, will be found about 110°
on the old one. The following Table exhibits the numer-
ical calculations illustrative of the principles inculcated
above.

NEW TABLE OF TEMPERATURE.

		Mercury.		Water.		Air.	Vapor.		
True equal intervals of temperature.	Roots, or intervals of temperature, com. dif. =.4105	Squares, or measures of temp. on merc. scale from freezing merc.	Same as preceding column, −40° or Farenheit's scale.	Common Farenheit's scale; or preceding column corrected for expansion of glass	Expansion of water as square of temp.	Expansion of air in geomet. progression ratio 1.0179	Force of vapor of water, geom. prog. ratio 1.321 In. M.	Force of vapor of ether, progr. ratio 1.2278 In. M.	Force of vapor from alcohol irregular Sp. Gr. .87 In. M.
−175°	0	0	−40°			692.—			
−68	4.3803	18.88	−21.12			837.6	.012	.78	
−58	4.7908	22.94	−17.06			852.5	.016	.96	
−48	5.2013	27.04	−12.96			867.7	.022	1.18	
−38	5.6118	31.58	−8.52			883.3	.028	1.45	
−28	6.0223	36.24	−3.76			899.—	.038	1.87	
−18	6.4328	41.34	1.34			915.2	.050	2.17	.47
−8	6.8433	46.78	6.78			931.5	.066	2.68	.52
2	7.2538	52.63	12.63		16	948.2	.087	3.30	.58
12	7.6643	58.74	18.74		9	965.2	.115	4.05	.64
22	8.0748	65.21	25.21		4	982.4	.151	4.97	.72
32	8.4853	72.—	32.—	32°	1	1000.—	.200	6.1	.80
42	8.8958	79.1	39.1	39.3	0	1017.9	.264	7.57	.93
52	9.3063	86.6	46.6	47.—	1	1036.1	.348	9.16	1.08
62	9.7108	94.44	54.44	55.—	4	1054.7	.461	11.22	1.3
72	10.1273	102.55	62.55	63.3	9	1073.5	.609	13.77	1.6
82	10.5378	111.04	71.04	72.—	16	1092.7	.804	16.85	2.1
92	10.9483	119.84	79.84	81.	25	1112.3	1.062	20.65	2.8
102	11.3588	129.02	89.02	90.4	36	1132.2	1.40	25.30	3.6
112	11.7693	138.49	98.49	100.1	49	1152.4	1.85	31.98	4.7
122	12.1798	148.3	108.3	110.—	64	1173.1	2.45	37.98	6.3
132	12.5903	158.5	118.5	120.1	81	1194.—	3.24	46.54	8.2
142	13.0008	169.—	129.—	130.4	100	1215.4	4.27	57.03	10.2
152	13.4113	179.9	139.9	141.1	121	1237.1	5.65	69.88	13.9
162	13.8218	191.—	151.—	152.—	144	1259.2	7.47	85.62	17.9
172	14.2323	202.4	162.4	163.2	169	1281.8	9.87	104.91	22.4
182	14.6428	214.4	174.4	175.—	196	1304.7	13.02	128.5	29.3
192	15.0533	226.5	186.5	186.9	225	1328.—	17.19	157.5	
202	15.4638	239	199.—	199.2	256	1351.8	22.70	193.—	
212	15.8743	252	212.	212.—	289	1376.—	30.00	236.5	
312	19.9793	399.1	359.1			1643.—	485.—		
412	24.0843	579.8	539.8			1962.—			
512	28.1893	794.7	754.7			2342.—			
612	32.2943	1043.—	1000.			2797.—			
712	36.3993	1325.	1285.			3339.			

Explanation of the Table.

The first column contains the degrees of temperature, of which there are supposed to be 180 between freezing and boiling water, according to Fahrenheit. The concurrence of so many analogies as have been mentioned, as well as experience, indicate that those degrees are produced by equal increments of the matter of heat, or caloric; but then it should be understood they are to be applied to a body of uniform bulk and capacity, such as air confined within a given space. If water, for instance, in its ordinary state, is to be raised successively through equal intervals of temperature, as measured by this scale, then unequal increments of heat will be requisite, by reason of its increased capacity. The first number in the column, —175°, denotes the point at which mercury freezes, hitherto marked —40°. The calculations are made for every 10° from —68° to 212°; above the last number, for every 100°. By comparing this column with the 5th, the correspondences of the new scale and the common one are perceived: the greatest difference between 32° and 212° is observable at 122° of the new scale, which agrees with 110° of the old, the difference being 12°; but below 32° and above 212°, the differences become more remarkable.

The 2d and 3d columns are two series, the one of roots, and the other of their squares. They are obtained thus; opposite 32°, in the first column, is placed in the 3d, 72°, being the number of degrees or equal parts in Fahrenheit's scale from freezing mercury to freezing water; and opposite 212° in the first is placed 252°in the 3d, being 212 + 40°, the number of degrees (or rather equal parts) between freezing mercury and boiling water. The square roots of these two numbers, 72° and 252°, are found and placed opposite to them in the second column. The number 8.4853 represents the relative quantity of real temperature between freezing mercury and freezing water; and the number 15.8743 represents the like between freezing mercury and boiling water; consequently the difference 7.3890 represents the relative quantity between freezing water and boiling water, and 7.3890 ÷ 18 = .4105 represents the quantity corresponding to each interval of 10°. By adding .4105 successively to 8.4853, or subtracting it from it, the rest of the numbers in the column are obtained, which are of course in arithmetical progression. The numbers in the 3d column are all obtained by squaring those of the 2d opposite to them. The unequal differences in the 3d column mark the expansions of mercury due to equal increments of temperature, by the theory. The inconvenient length of the table prevents its being carried down by intervals of 10° to the point of freezing mercury, which however is found to be at −175°.

The 4th column is the same as the 3d, with the difference of 40°, to make it conform to the common method of numbering on Fahrenheit's scale.

The 5th column is the 4th corrected, on account of the unequal expansion of Glass: The *apparent* expansion of mercury in glass is less than the *real*, by the expansion of the glass itself; this, however, would not disturb the law of expansion of the liquid, both apparent and real being subject to the same, *provided the glass expands equally;* this will be shown hereafter. But it has been shown by De Luc, that glass expands less in the lower half of the scale than the higher; this must occasion the mercury apparently to expand more in the lower half than what is dictated by the law of expansion. By calculating from De Luc's data, I find, that the mercury in the middle of the scale, or 122°, ought to be found nearly 3° higher than would be, were it not for this increase. Not however to over-rate the effect, I have taken it only at 1.7°, making the number 108.3° in the 4th column, 110° in the 5th, and the rest of the column is corrected accordingly. The numbers in this column cannot well be extended much beyond the interval from freezing to boiling water, for want of experiments on the expansion of glass. By viewing this column along with the 1st, the quantity of the supposed error in the common scale may be perceived; and any observations on the old thermometer may be reduced to the new.

The 6th column contains the squares of the natural series 1, 2, 3, etc. representing the expansion of water by equal intervals of temperature. Thus, if a portion of water at 42° expands a quantity represented by 289, at the boiling temperature, then at 52° it will be found to have expanded 1, at 62°, 4 parts, etc., etc. Water expands by cold or the abstraction of heat in the same way below the point of greatest density, as will be illustrated when we come to consider the absolute expansion of bodies. The apparent greatest density too does not happen at 39.3° old scale; but about 42°; and the greatest real density is at or near 36° of the same.

The 7th column contains a series of numbers in geometrical progression, denoting the expansion of air, or elastic fluids. The volume at 32° is taken 1000, and at 212°, 1376 according to Gay Lussac's and my own experiments. As for the expansion at intermediate degrees, General Roi makes the temperature at midway of total expansion, $116^1/_2$° old scale; from the results of my former experiments (Manch. Mem. Vol. 5, Part 2, page 599), the temperature may be estimated at $119^1/_2$°; but I had not then an opportunity of having air at 32°. By more recent experiments I am convinced that dry air of 32° will expand the same quantity from that to 117° or 118° of common scale, as from the last term to 212°. According to the theory in the above Table it appears, that air of 117° will be 1188, or have acquired one half its total expansion. Now if the theory accord so well with experiment in the middle of the interval, we cannot expect it to do otherwise in the inter-mediate points.

The 8th column contains the force of aqueous vapors in contact with water expressed in inches of mercury, at the respective temperatures. It constitutes a geometrical progression; the numbers opposite 32° and 212°, namely, .200 and 30.0 are derived from experiments, (ibid. page 559) and the rest are determined from theory. It is re-markable that those numbers do not differ from the table just referred to, which was the result of actual experience, so much as 2° in any part; a difference that might even exist between two thermometers of the same kind.

The 9th column exhibits the force of the vapor of sulphuric ether in contact with liquid ether; which is a geometrical progression, having a less ratio than that of water. Since writing my former Essay on the Force of Steam, I am enabled to correct one of the conclusions therein contained; the error was committed by trusting to the accuracy of the common mercurial thermometer. Ex-perience confirmed me that the force of vapor from water of nearly 212°, varied from a change of temperature as much as vapor from ether of nearly 100°. Hence I deduced this general law, namely, "that the variation of the force of vapor from all liquids is the same for the same variation of temperature, reckoning from vapor of any given force." But I now find that 30° of temperature in the lower part of the common scale is much more than 30° in the higher: and therefore the vapors of ether and water are not subject to the same change of force by equal increments of

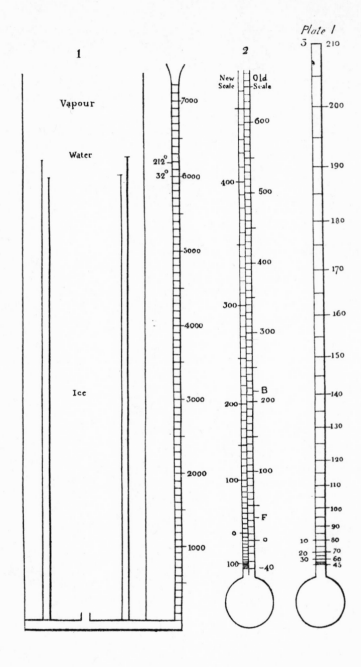

Plate 1

PLATE I. Fig. 1. is intended to illustrate the author's ideas on the subject of the capacities of bodies for heat. See Chapter I, Section 1, "On Temperature." There are three cylindrical vessels placed one within another, having no communication but over their margins; the innermost is connected with a lateral and parallel tube graduated, and supposed to represent the degrees of a thermometer, the scale of which commences at absolute cold; if a liquid (supposed to represent heat) be poured into the tube, it will flow into the inner vessel, through an aperture at the bottom, and rise to the same level in the vessel and the tube. Equal increments of heat in this case are supposed to produce equal increments of temperature. When the temperature has arrived at a certain point (suppose 6000°) the body may be supposed to change its solid form to the liquid, as from ice to water, in which case its capacity for heat is increased, and is to be represented by the second vessel. A considerable portion of liquid must then be poured into the tube before any rise will be perceived, because it flows over the margin of the innermost vessel into the lateral cavity of the second; at length it reaches the level, and then a proportional rise will ensue, till the body becomes converted into an elastic fluid, when the thermometer again becomes stationary—while, a great portion of heat is entering into the body, now assuming a new capacity.

Fig. 2. is a comparative view of the old and new divisions of the scale of the mercurial thermometer. See New Table of Temperature (Chapter I, Section 1). The interval from freezing to boiling water is 180° on both scales, and the extremes are numbered 32° and 212° respectively. There are no other points of temperature in which the two scales can agree.

Fig. 3. is a view of the divisions of a water thermometer, conformably to the new scale of the mercurial; the lowest point is at 45°; the intervals from 45° upwards, to 55°, 65°, 75°, etc. are as the numbers 1, 4, 9, etc. Also, 30° and 0° coincide, as do 20° and 70°, etc.

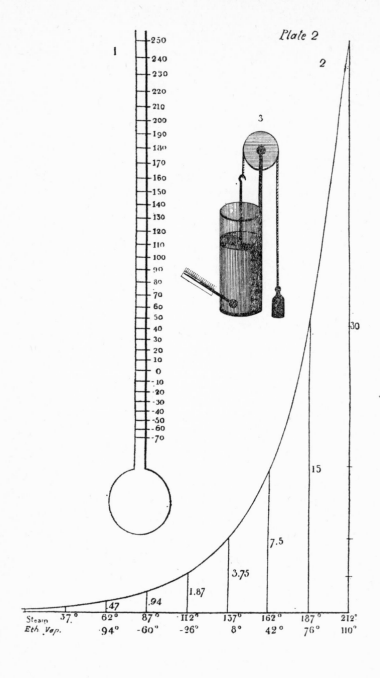

Plate 2

1

2

3

30

15

7.5

3.75

1.87

.94

.47

Steam	37°	62°	87°	112°	137°	162°	187°	212°
Eth. Vap.		.94°	-60°	-26°	8°	42°	76°	110°

PLATE II. Fig. 1. represents an air thermometer, or the expansion of air by heat; the numbers are Fahrenheit's, and the intervals are such as represented in the 7th column of the New Table of Temperature (Chapter I, Section 1).

Fig. 2. is the logarithmic curve, the ordinates of which are erected at equal intervals, and diminish progressively by the ratio $1/2$. The intervals of the abscissa or base of the curve, represent equal intervals of temperature (25° for steam or aqueous vapor, and 34° for ethereal vapor) the ordinates represent inches of mercury, the weight of which is equal to the force of steam at the temperature. See the 8th and 9th columns of table, at page 11. Thus the force of steam at 212°, and of ethereal vapor at 110°, new scale, is equal to 30 inches of mercury; at 187° the force of steam is half as much, or 15 inches, and at 76°, that of ethereal vapor is also 15 inches, etc.

Fig. 3. is a device suggested by Mr. Ewart, to illustrate the idea which I have developed in the section on the temperature of the atmosphere. It is a cylindrical vessel closed at one end and open at the other, having a moveable piston sliding within it: the vessel is supposed to contain air, and a weight is connected with the piston as a counterpoise to it. There is also a thermometer supposed to pass through the side of the vessel, and to be cemented into it. Now if we may suppose the piston to move without friction, and the vessel to be taken up into the atmosphere, the piston will gradually ascend, and suffer the air within to dilate, so as to correspond every where with the exterior air in density. This dilatation tends to diminish the temperature of the air within (provided no heat is acquired from the vessel.) Such an instrument would show what the theory requires, namely, that the temperature of the air within would every where in the same vertical column agree with that without, though the former would not receive or part with any heat absolutely, or in any manner communicate with the external air.

temperature. The truth is, vapor from water, ether and other liquids, increases in force in geometrical progression to the temperature; but the ratio is different in different fluids. Ether as manufactured in the large way, appears to be a very homogeneous liquid. I have purchased it in London, Edinburgh, Glasgow and Manchester, at very different times, of precisely the same quality in respect to its vapor; namely, such as when thrown up into a barometer would depress the mercury 15 inches at the temperature of 68°. Nor does it lose any of its effect by time; I have now a barometer with a few drops of ether on the mercury, that has continued with invaried efficacy for eight or nine years. The numbers in the column between the temperatures of 20° and 80°, are the results of repeated observations on the above ether barometer for many years; those above and below are obtained from direct experiment as far as from 0 to 212°; the low ones were found by subjecting the vacuum of the barometer to an artificial cold mixture; and the higher ones were found in the manner related in my former Essays: only the highest force has been considerably increased from what I formerly had it, in consequence of supplying the manometer with more ether; it having been found to leave little or no liquid when at the temperature of 212°; and in order to obtain the maximum effect it is indispensible to have a portion of liquid remaining in contact with the vapor.

The 10th column shows the force of vapor from alcohol, or rather common spirit of wine, determined by experiment in the same way as the vapor of water. This is not a geometrical progression, probably because the liquid is not pure and homogeneous. I suspect the elastic fluid in this case is a mixture of aqueous and alcoholic vapor.

On Expansion by Heat

One important effect of heat is the expansion of bodies of every kind. Solids are least expanded; liquids more; and elastic fluids most of all. The quantities of increase in bulk have in many instances been determined; but partly through the want of a proper thermometer, little general information has been derived from particular experiments. The force necessary to counteract the expansion has not been ascertained, except in the case of elastic fluids; but there is no doubt it is very great. The quantity and law of expansion of all permanent elastic fluids have already been given; it remains then to advert to liquid and solid bodies.

In order to understand the expansion of liquids, it is expedient to premise certain propositions:

1st. Suppose a thermometrical vessel of glass, metal, etc., were filled with any liquid up to a certain mark in the stem; and that it was known the vessel and the liquid had precisely the same expansion, bulk for bulk, with the same change of temperature; then it must be evident upon a little consideration, that whatever change of temperature took place, the liquid must remain at the same mark.

2. Suppose as before, except that both bodies expand uniformly with the temperature, but the liquid at a greater rate than the vessel: then it is evident by an increase of temperature, the liquid would appear to ascend uniformly a quantity equal to the difference of the absolute expansion of the two bodies.

3. Suppose as in the last case, but that the liquid expands at a less rate than the vessel; the liquid would then descend, and that uniformly by an increase of temperature, a quantity equal to the difference of the absolute expansions.

4. Suppose as before, only the vessel now expands uniformly, and the liquid with a velocity uniformly accelerated, commencing from rest; in this case if temperature be added uniformly, the liquid will appear to descend with a velocity uniformly retarded to a certain point, there to be stationary, and afterwards to ascend with an uniformly accelerated velocity, of the same sort as the former. For, as the velocity with which the liquid expands is uniformly accelerative, it must successively pass through all degrees from 0 to any assigned quantity, and must therefore in some moment be the same as that of the vessel, and therefore, for that moment, the liquid must appear stationary: previously to that time the liquid must have descended by the third proposition, and must afterwards ascend, by the 2d. but not uniformly. Let the absolute space expanded by the liquid at the moment of equal velocities be denoted by 1, then that of the vessel in the same time must be 2; because the velocity acquired by an uniformly accelerating force, is such as to move a body

through twice the space in the same time. It follows then that the liquid must have sunk 1, being the excess of the expansion of the vessel above that of the liquid. Again, let another portion of temperature equal to the former be added, then the absolute expansion of the liquid will be 4, reckoned from the commencement; and the expansion of the vessel also 4: the place of the liquid will be the same as at first, and therefore it must apparently ascend 1 by the 2d portion. Let a third portion of heat equal to one of the former be added, and it will make the total expansion of the liquid 9, or give 5 additional expansion, from which deducting 2, that of the vessel, there remains 3 for the apparent expansion by the 3d portion; in like manner 5 will be due for the 4th, and 7 for the 5th, etc., being the series of odd numbers. But the aggregate of these forms a series of squares, as is well known. Hence the apparent expansion will proceed by the same law as the real, only starting from a higher temperature. If the law of expansion of the liquid be such that either the addition or abstraction of temperature, that is, either heat or cold produces expansion alike, reckoned from the point of greatest density; then the apparent expansion will still be guided by the same law as the real. For, if when the liquid is at the lowest point of the scale, we withdraw a portion of heat, it ascends to 1; or is in the circumstance of greatest density, and no expansion as at the commencement; if then we withdraw another portion, it will expand 1 by hypothesis, but the vessel will contract 2, which must make the apparent expansion of the liquid 3; by another portion it will be 5, by another 7, etc., as before.

The truth of the above proposition may be otherwise shown thus:

Let 1, 4, 9, 16, 25, etc., represent the absolute expansions of the liquid, and p, $2p$, $3p$, $4p$, $5p$, etc., those of the vessel by equal increments of temperature, then $1-p$, $4-2p$, $9-3p$, $16-4p$, $25-5p$, etc., will represent the apparent expansion of the liquid; the differences of these last quantities, namely $3-p$, $5-p$, $7-p$, $9-p$, etc., form a series in arithmetical progression, the common difference of which is 2. But it is demonstrated by algebraists, that the differences of a series of square numbers, whose roots are in arithmetical progression, form an arithmetical progression, and that the common difference of the terms of this progression is equal to twice the square of the difference of the roots. Hence, as $2 =$ twice the square of 1, we have the above arithmetical series $3-p$, $5-p$, etc., equal to the differences of a series of squares, the common difference of the roots of which is 1.

Now to apply these principles: solid bodies are generally allowed to expand uniformly within the common range of temperature: at all events the quantity is so small compared with the expansion of liquids, such as water, that the deviation from uniformity cannot require notice in many cases. Water being supposed to expand according to the square of the temperature from that of greatest density, we may derive the following conclusions.

Cor. 1. The laws of uniformly accelerated motion, are the same as those of the expansion of water, whether absolute or apparent, the time in one denoting the temperature in the other, and the space denoting the expansion: that is, if $t =$ time or temperature, $v =$ velocity, and $s =$ space or expansion: then,

$$t^2, \text{ or } tv, \text{ or } v^2 \text{ are as } s.$$

$$\tfrac{1}{2} t v = s$$

$$v \text{ is as } t$$

$$\dot{s} \text{ is as } 2 t \dot{t}$$

$$\dot{s} \text{ is as } t, \dot{t} \text{ being supposed constant, etc.}$$

Cor. 2. The real expansion of water from maximum density for any number of degrees of temperature, is the same as the apparent expansion from apparent greatest density in any vessel for the same number of degrees. For instance, if water in a glass vessel appears to be of greatest density, or descends lowest at 42° of common scale, and appears to expand $1/_{25}$ of its first volume from thence to 212° then it may be inferred that the real expansion of water from greatest density by 170° is $1/_{25}$ of its volume; so that the absolute expansion of water is determinable this way, without knowing either at what temperature its density is greatest, or the expansion of the vessel containing it.

Cor. 3. If the expansion of any vessel can be obtained; then may the temperature at which water is of greatest density be obtained; and *vice versa.* This furnishes us with an excellent method of ascertaining both the relative and absolute expansion of all solid bodies that can be formed into vessels capable of holding water.

Cor. 4. If the apparent expansion of water from maximum density for 180° were to be equalled by a body expanding uniformly, its velocity must be equal to that of water at 90°, or mid-way. And if any solid body be found to have the same expansion as water at 10° from max. density; then its expansion for 180° must be $1/_9$ of that of water, etc. Because in water v is as t, etc.

By graduating several glass thermometer vessels, filling them with water, exposing them to different temperatures, and comparing results, I have found the *apparent* expansion of water in glass for every 10° of the common or old scale (as I shall henceforward call it) and the new one, as under.

The whole expansion of water for 180° of temperature, reckoned from the point of greatest density, appears from the 2d Table to be $1/_{21.5}$, or $21^1/_2$ parts become $22^1/_2$.

EXPANSION OF WATER.

OLD SCALE.		NEW SCALE.	
		5°	100227
12°	100236	15	100129
22	100090	25	100057
32	100022	35	100014
42	100000	45	100000
52	100021	55	100014+
62	100083	65	100057
72	100180	75	100129
82	100312	85	100227
92	100477	95	100359
102	100672	105	100517
112	100880	115	100704
122	101116	125	100919
132	101367	135	101163
142	101638	145	101436
152	101934	155	101738
162	102245	165	102068
172	102575	175	102426
182	102916	185	102814
192	103265	195	103231
202	103634	205	103676
212	104012	215	104150
		225	104658

In the Edinburgh Philosophical Transactions for 1804, Dr. Hope has given a paper on the contraction of water by heat in low temperatures. (See also Nicholson's Journal, Vol. 12.) In this paper we find an excellent history of facts and opinions relative to this remarkable question in physics, with original experiments. There appear to have been two opinions respecting the temperature at which water obtains its maximum density; the one stating it to be at the freezing point, or 32°; the other at 40°. Previously to the publication of the above essay, I had embraced the opinion that the point was 32°, chiefly from some experiments about to be related. Dr. Hope argued from his own experiments in favor of the other opinion. My attention was again turned to the subject, and upon re-examination of facts, I found them all to concur in giving the point of greatest density at the temperature 36°, or mid-way between the points formerly supposed. In two letters inserted in Nicholson's Journal, Vol. 13 and 14, I endeavored to show that Dr. Hope's experiments supported this conclusion and no other. I shall now show that my own experiments on the apparent expansion of water in different vessels, coincide with them in establishing the same conclusion.

The results of my experiments, without those deductions, were published in Nicholson's Journal, Vol. 10. Since then some small additions and corrections have been made. It may be observed that small vessels, capable of holding one or two ounces of water, were made of the different materials, and such as that glass tubes could be cemented into them when full of water, so as to resemble and act as a common thermometer. The observations follow:

		Water stationary.	Corresponding points of expansion.
1	Brown earthen ware at 38°		at 32° & 44°
2	Common white ware, and } stone ware	40	32 & 48+
3	Flint glass	42	32 & 52¹/₂
4	Iron	42+	32 & 53−
5	Copper	45+	32 & 59
6	Brass	45¹/₂	32 & 60−
7	Pewter	46	32 & 60¹/₂
8	Zinc	48	32 & 64+
9	Lead	49	32 & 67

As the expansion of earthen ware by heat has never before been ascertained, we cannot make use of the first and second experiments to find the temperature of greatest density; all that we can learn from them is, that the point must be below 38°.

According to Smeaton, glass expands $1/1200$ in length for 180° of temperature; consequently it expands $1/400$ in bulk. But water expands $1/21.5$ or rather more than 18 times as much; therefore the mean velocity of the expansion of water (which is that at 90°, or half way) is 18 times more than that of glass, which is equal to the expansion of water at 42°; this last must therefore be $1/18$ of the former; consequently water of 42° has passed through $1/18$ of the temperature to the mean, or $1/18$ of 90° = 5°, of new scale = 4° of old scale, above the temperature at which it is absolutely of greatest density. This conclusion however cannot be accurate; for, it appears from the preceding paragraph that the temperature must be below 38°. The inaccuracy arises, I have no doubt, from the expansion of glass having been under-rated by Smeaton; not from any mistake of his, but from the peculiar nature of glass. Rods and tubes of glass are seldom if ever properly annealed; hence they are in a state of violent energy, and often break spontaneously or with a slight scratch of a file: tubes have been found to expand more than rods, and it might be expected that thin bulbs should expand more still, because they do not require annealing; hence too the great strength of thin glass, its being less brittle, and more susceptible of sudden transitions of temperature. From the above experiments it seems that the expansion due to glass, such as the bulbs of ordinary thermometers, is very little less than that of iron.

Iron expands nearly $1/_{800}$ in length by 180° of heat, or $1/_{263}$ in bulk; this is nearly $1/_{12}$ of the expansion of water; hence $90 \div 12 = 7^1/_2°$ of true mean temperature $= 6°$ of common scale; this taken from $42+°$, leaves 36° of common scale for the temperature at which water is of greatest density.

Copper is to iron as 3:2 in expansion; therefore if 6° be the allowance for iron, that for copper must be 9°; hence $45°-9°=36°$, for the temperature as before.

Brass expands about $1/_{20}$ more than copper; hence we shall have $45^1/_2°-9^1/_2 = 36°$, for the temperature as above.

Fine pewter is to iron as 11:6 in expansion, according to Smeaton; hence $46°-11°=35°$, for the temperature as derived from the vessel of pewter: but this being a mixed metal, it is not so much to be relied upon.

Zinc expands $1/_{113}$ in bulk for 180°, if we may credit Smeaton: hence water expands $5^1/_4$ times as much as zinc; and $90 \div 5^1/_4 = 17°$ of new scale $= 13^1/_2°$ of old scale; whence $48° - 13^1/_2° = 34^1/_2°$ for the temperature derived from zinc. It seems highly probable that in this case the expansion of the vessel is over-rated; it was found to be less than that of lead, whereas Smeaton makes it more.

The vessel was made of the patent malleable zinc of Hodson and Sylvester. Perhaps it contains a portion of tin, which will account for the deviation.

Lead expands $1/_{116}$ of its bulk for 180°; water therefore expands about $5^1/_2$ times as much; this gives $90 \div 5^1/_2 = 16^1/_2°$ of new scale $= 13°$ of old scale; whence $49°-13° = 36°$, as before.

From these experiments it seems demonstrated, that the greatest density of water is at or near the 36° of the old scale, and 37° or 38° of the new scale: and further, that the expansion of thin glass is nearly the same as that of iron, whilst that of stone ware is $2/_3$, and brown earthen ware $1/_3$ of the same.

The apparent expansion of mercury in a thermometrical glass for 180° I find to be .0163 from 1. That of thin glass may be stated at .0037 $= 1/_{270}$, which is rather less than iron, $1/_{265}$. Consequently the real expansion of mercury from 32° to 212° is equal to the sum of these $= .02$ or $1/_{50}$. De Luc makes it, .01836, and most other authors make it less; because they have all under-rated the expansion of glass. Hence we derive this proportion, .0163:180° :: .0037: 41° nearly, which expresses the effect of the expansion of glass on the mercurial thermometer: that is, the mercury would rise 41° higher on the scale at the temperature of boiling water, if the glass had no expansion. De Luc makes the expansion of a glass tube from 32° to 212° $= .00083$ in length, and from 32° to 122° only .00035. This inequality in part at least, I apprehend, from the want of equilibrium in the original fixation of glass tubes, the outside being hard when the inside is soft.

Liquids may be denominated pure when they are not decomposed by heat and cold. Solutions of salts in water cannot be deemed such; because their constitution is affected by temperature. Thus, if a solution of sulphate of soda in water be cooled, a portion of the salt crystallizes, and leaves the remaining liquid less saline than before; whereas water and mercury, when partially congealed, leave the remaining liquid of the same quality as before. Most acid liquids are similar to saline solutions in this respect. Alcohol as we commonly have it, is a solution of pure alcohol in a greater or less portion of water: and probably would be affected by congelation like other solutions. Ether is one of the purest liquids, except water and mercury. Oils, both fixed and volatile, are probably for the most part impure, in the sense we use it. Notwithstanding these observations, it is remarkable how nearly those liquids approximate to the law of expansion observed in water and mercury. Few authors have made experiments on these subjects; and their results in several instances are incorrect. My own investigations have been chiefly directed to water and mercury; but it may be proper to give the results of my inquiries on the other liquids as far as they have been prosecuted.

Alcohol expands about $1/9$ of its bulk for 180°, from -8 to 172°. The relative expansions of this liquid are given by De Luc from 32° to 212°; but the results of my experiments do not seem to accord with his. According to him alcohol expands 35 parts for the first 90°, and 45 parts for the second 90°. The strength of his alcohol was such as to fire gun-powder: but this is an indefinite test. From my experiments I judge it must have been very weak. I find 1000 parts of alcohol of .817 sp. gravity at the temperature 50° became 1079 at the temperature 170° of the common mercurial scale: at 110° the alcohol is at 1039, or half a division below the true mean. When the sp. gravity is .86, I find 1000 parts at 50° become 1072 at 170°; at 110° the bulk is 1035 +, whence the disproportion of the two parts of the scale is not so much in this case as 35 to 37. When the sp. gravity is .937, I find 1000 parts become 1062 at 170°, and 1029$^1/_2$ at 110°; hence the ratio of the expansion becomes 29$^1/_2$ to 32$^1/_2$. When the sp. gravity is .967, answering to 75 per cent. water, I find 1000 parts at 50° become 1040 at 170°, and 1017$^1/_2$ at 110°, giving a ratio of 35 to 45; which is the same as De Luc gives for alcohol. It is true he takes an interval of temperature = 180°, and I take one for 120° only; but still it is impossible to reconcile our results. As the expansion of alcohol from 172° to 212° must have been conjectural, perhaps he has over-rated it. In reporting these results I have not taken into account the expansion of the glass vessel, a large thermometrical bulb, containing about 750 grains of water, and having a tube proportionally wide; consequently the real expansions must be considered as more rather than less than above stated. The graduation of the vessel having been repeatedly examined, and being the same that was used in determining the expansion of water, I can place confidence in the results. Particular care was taken in these experiments to have the bulb and stem both immersed in water of the proposed temperature.

As alcohol of .817 sp. gravity contains at least 8 per cent. water, it is fair to infer from the above that a thermometer of pure alcohol would in no apparent degree differ from one of mercury in the interval of temperature from 50° to 170°. But when we consider that the relative expansions of glass, mercury and alcohol for this interval, are as 1, 5$^1/_2$ and 22 respectively, it must be obvious that the inequality of the expansion of glass in the higher and lower parts of the scale, which tends to equalize the apparent expansion of mercury, has little influence on alcohol, by reason of its comparative insignificance. Hence it may be presumed that a spirit thermometer would be more equable in its divisions than a mercurial one, in a vessel of uniform expansion. This it ought to be by theory, because the point of greatest density or congelation of alcohol is below that of mercury.

Water being densest at 36°, and alcohol at a very remote temperature below, it was to be expected that mixtures of these would be densest at intermediate temperatures, and those higher as the water prevailed; thus we find the disproportion, so observable in the expansion of water, growing greater and greater in the mixtures as they approach to pure water.

Water saturated with common salt expands as follows: 1000 parts at 32° become 1050 at 212°; at 122° it is nearly 1023, which gives the ratio of 23 to 27 for the corresponding equal intervals of mercury. This is nearly the same as De Luc's ratio of 36.3 to 43.7. This solution is said to congeal at −7°, and probably expands nearly as the square of the temperature from that point. It differs from most other saline solutions in regard to its expansion by temperature.

Olive and linseed oils expand about 8 per cent. by 180° of temperature; De Luc finds the expansion of olive oil nearly correspond to mercury; with me it is more disproportionate, nearly agreeing with water saturated with salt.

Oil of turpentine expands about 7 per cent. for 180°; it expands much more in the higher than in the lower part of the scale, as it ought to do, the freezing point being stated at 14 or 16°. The ratio is somewhere about 3 to 5. Several authors have it that oil of turpentine boils at 560°; I do not know how the mistake originated; but it boils below 212°, like the rest of the essential oils.

Sulphuric acid, sp. gravity 1.85, expands about 6 per cent. from 32° to 212°. It accords with mercury as nearly as possible in every part of the scale. Dr. Thomson says the freezing point of acid of this strength is at −36° or below; whence it accords with the same law as water and mercury. I find that even the glacial sulphuric acid, or that of 1.78 sp. gravity, which remains congealed at 45°, expands uniformly, or nearly like the other, whilst it continues liquid.

Nitric acid, sp. gravity 1.40, expands about 11 per cent. from 32° to 212°; the expansion is nearly of the same rate as that of mercury, the disproportion not being more than 27 to 28 or thereabouts. The freezing point of acid of this strength is near the freezing point of mercury.

Muriatic acid, sp. gravity 1.137, expands about 6 per cent. from 32° to 212°; it is more disproportionate than nitric acid, as might be expected, being so largely diluted with water. The ratio is nearly 6 to 7.

Sulphuric ether expands after the rate of 7 per cent. for 180° of temperature. I have only compared the expansion of this liquid with that of mercury from 60° to 90°. In this interval it accords so nearly with mercury that I could perceive no sensible difference in their rates. It is said to freeze at −46°.

From what has been observed it may be seen that water expands less than most other liquids; yet it ought to be considered as having in reality the greatest rate of expansion. Alcohol and nitric acid, which appear to expand so much, do not excel, or even equal water, if we estimate their expansion from the temperature of greatest density, and compare them with water in like circumstances. It is because we begin with them at 100 or 200° above the point of greatest density, and observe their expansion for 180° further, that they appear to expand so largely. Water, if it continued liquid, would expand three times as much in the *second* interval of 180° as it does in the first, reckoning from 36°.

EXPANSION OF SOLIDS

No general law has hitherto been discovered respecting the expansion of solid bodies; but as elastic fluids and liquids appear to be subject to their respective laws in this particular, we may confidently expect that solids will be found so too. As it may be presumed that solids undergo no change of form, by the abstraction of heat, it is probable that whatever the law may be, it will respect the point at which temperature commences, or what may be called, absolute cold. It is not our present business to enquire how low this point is; but it may be observed that every phenomenon indicates it to be very low, or much lower than is commonly apprehended. Perhaps it may hereafter be demonstrated that the interval of temperature from 32° to 212° of Fahrenheit, constitutes the 10th, 15th, or 20th interval from absolute cold. Judging from analogy, we may conjecture that the expansion of solids is progressively increasing with the temperature; but whether it is a geometrical progression as elastic fluids, or one increasing as the square of the temperature, like liquids, or as the 3d or any power of the temperature, still if it be estimated from absolute cold, it must appear to be nearly uniform, or in arithmetical progression to the temperature, for so small and remote an interval of temperature as that between freezing and boiling water. The truth of this observation will appear from the following calculation: let us suppose the interval in question to be the 15th; then the real temperature of freezing water will be 2520°, the mid-way to boiling 2610°, and boiling water 2700°, reckoned from absolute cold.

	Dif.			Dif.
$14^2 = 196$			$14^3 = 2744$	
	$—14^1/_4$			$—304^5/_8$
$14^1/_2{}^2 = 210^1/_4$			$14^1/_2{}^3 = 3048^5/_8$	
	$—14^3/_4$			$—326^3/_8$
$15^2 = 225$			$15^3 = 3375$	

Now the differences above represent the ratios of expansion for 90° of temperature; they are in the former case as 57 to 59, and in the latter as 14 to 15 nearly. But the temperature being supposed to be measured by the new scale, the mean is about 110° of the old scale; therefore the expansion of solids should be as 57 or 14 from 32° to 110°, and as 59 or 15 from 110° to 212° of the old scale. If these conjectures be right, the expansion of solids ought to be something greater in the lower part of the old scale, and something less in the higher part. Experience at present does not enable us to decide the question. For all practical purposes we may adopt the notion of the equable expansion of solids. Only glass has been found to expand increasingly with the temperature, and this arises probably from its peculiar constitution, as has been already observed.

Various pyrometers, or instruments for measuring the expansion of solids, have been invented, of which accounts may be seen in books of natural philosophy. Their object is to ascertain the expansion in length of any proposed subject. The longitudinal expansion being found, that of the bulk may be derived from it, and will be three times as much. Thus, if a bar of 1000 expand to 1001 by a certain temperature; then 1000 cubic inches of the same will become 1003 by the same temperature.

The following Table exhibits the expansion of the principal subjects hitherto determined, for 180° of temperature; that is, from 32° to 212° of Fahrenheit. The bulk and length of the articles at 32° are denoted by 1.

SOLIDS.	EXPANSION. In bulk.	In length.
Brown earthen ware	$.0012 = \frac{1}{800}$	$\frac{1}{2400}$
Stone ware	$.0025 = \frac{1}{400}$	$\frac{1}{1200}$
Glass—rods and tubes	$.0025 = \frac{1}{400}$	$\frac{1}{1200}$ †
——bulbs (thin)	$.0037 = \frac{1}{270}$	$\frac{1}{810}$
Platinum	$.0026 = \frac{1}{385}$	$\frac{1}{1155}$ ‡
Steel	$.0034 = \frac{1}{294}$	$\frac{1}{882}$ †
Iron	$.0038 = \frac{1}{263}$	$\frac{1}{790}$ †
Gold	$.0042 = \frac{1}{238}$	$\frac{1}{714}$ *
Bismuth	$.0042 = \frac{1}{238}$	$\frac{1}{714}$ †
Copper	$.0051 = \frac{1}{196}$	$\frac{1}{588}$ †
Brass	$.0056 = \frac{1}{178}$	$\frac{1}{533}$ †
Silver	$.0060 = \frac{1}{160}$	$\frac{1}{480}$ *
Fine Pewter	$.0068 = \frac{1}{140}$	$\frac{1}{440}$ †
Tin	$.0074 = \frac{1}{133}$	$\frac{1}{400}$ †
Lead	$.0086 = \frac{1}{115}$	$\frac{1}{348}$ †
Zinc	$.0093 = \frac{1}{108}$	$\frac{1}{322}$ †

LIQUIDS.		
Mercury	$.0200 = \frac{1}{50}$	
Water	$.0466 = \frac{1}{21.5}$	
Water sat. with salt	$.0500 = \frac{1}{20}$	
Sulphuric acid	$.0600 = \frac{1}{17}$	
Muriatic Acid	$.0600 = \frac{1}{17}$	
Oil of turpentine	$.0700 = \frac{1}{14}$	
Ether	$.0700 = \frac{1}{14}$	
Fixed oils	$.0800 = \frac{1}{12.5}$	
Alcohol	$.110 = \frac{1}{9}$	
Nitric acid	$.110 = \frac{1}{9}$	

ELASTIC FLUIDS.		
Gases of all kinds	$.376 = \frac{3}{8}$	

* Ellicott.   † Smeaton.   ‡ Borda.

Wedgwood's Thermometer.

The spirit thermometer serves to measure the greatest degrees of cold we are acquainted with, and the mercurial thermometer measures 400° above boiling water, by the old scale, or about 250° by the new one, at which temperature the mercury boils. This is short of red heat, and very far short of the highest attainable temperature. An instrument to measure high temperatures is very desirable; and Mr. Wedgwood's is the best we have yet; but there is still great room for improvement. Small cylindrical pieces of clay, composed in the manner of earthen ware, and slightly baked, are the thermometrical pieces. When used, one of them is exposed in a crucible to the heat proposed to be measured, and after cooling, it is found to be contracted, in proportion to the heat previously sustained; the quantity of contraction being measured, indicates the temperature. The whole range of this thermometer is divided into 240 equal degrees, each of which is calculated to be equal to 130° of Fahrenheit. The lowest, or 0, is found about 1077° of Fahrenheit (supposing the common scale continued above boiling mercury,) and the highest 32277°. According to the new views of temperature in the preceding pages, there is reason to think these numbers are much too large.

The following Table exhibits some of the more re-markable temperatures in the whole range, according to the present state of our knowledge.

	Wedg.
Extremity of Wedgwood's thermometer	240°
Pig iron, cobalt and nickel, melt from 130° to	150
Greatest heat of a Smith's forge	125
Furnaces for glass and earthen ware, from 40 to	124
Gold melts	32
Settling heat of flint glass	29
Silver melts	28
Copper melts	27
Brass melts	21
Diamond burns	14
Red heat visible in day-light	0

	Fahrenheit. old scale.
Hydrogen and charcoal burn 800° to	1000°
Antimony melts	809
Zinc	700
Lead	612
Mercury boils	600
Linseed oil boils	600
Sulphuric acid boils	590
Bismuth	476
Tin	442
Sulphur burns slowly	303
Nitric acid boils	240
Water and essential oils boil	212
Bismuth 5 parts, tin 3 and lead 2, melt	210
Alcohol boils	174
Bees wax melts	142
Ether boils	98
Blood heat 96° to	98
Summer heat in this climate 75° to	80
Sulphuric acid (1.78) when congealed, begins to melt	45
Mixture of ice and water	32
Milk freezes	30
Vinegar freezes	28
Strong wines freeze about	20
Snow 3 parts, salt 2	−7
Cold observed on the snow at Kendal, 1791	−10
Ditto at Glasgow, 1780	−23
Mercury freezes	−39
Greatest artificial cold observed	−90

Section 3

On the Specific Heat of Bodies

If the whole quantity of heat in a measure of water of a certain temperature be denoted by 1, that in the same measure of mercury will be denoted by .5 nearly: hence the specific heats of water and mercury, *of equal bulks,* may be signified by 1 and .5 respectively.

If the specific heats be taken from *equal weights* of the two liquids; then they will be denoted by 1 and .04 nearly; because we have to divide .5 by 13.6, the specific gravity of mercury.

That bodies differ much in their specific heats, is manifest from the following facts.

1. If a measure of mercury of 212° be mixed with a measure of water of 32°, the mixture will be far *below* the mean temperature.

2. If a measure of mercury of 32° be mixed with a measure of water of 212°, the mixture will be far *above* the mean.

3. If two equal and like vessels be filled, the one with

hot water, the other with hot mercury; the latter will cool in about half the time of the former.

4. If a measure of sulphuric acid be mixed with a measure of water of the same temperature, the mixture will assume a temperature about 240° higher.

These facts clearly show that bodies have various affinities for heat, and that those bodies which have the strongest attraction or affinity for heat, possess the most of it in like circumstances; in other words, they are said to have the greatest *capacity for heat,* or the greatest specific heat. It is found too that the same body changes its capacity for heat, or apparently assumes a new affinity, with a change of form. This no doubt arises from a new arrangement or disposition of its ultimate particles, by which their atmospheres of heat are influenced: Thus a solid body, as ice, on becoming liquid, acquires a larger capacity for heat, even though its bulk is diminished; and a liquid, as water, acquires a larger capacity for heat on being converted into an elastic fluid; this last increase is occasioned, we may conceive, solely by its being increased in bulk, in consequence of which every atom of liquid possesses a larger sphere than before.

A very important inquiry is, whether the same body in the same state undergoes any change of capacity by change of temperature. Does water, for instance, at 32° possess the same capacity for heat, as at 212°, and through all the intermediate degrees? Dr. Crawford, and most writers after him, contend, that the capacities of bodies in such circumstances are *nearly* permanent. As an outline of doctrine this may be admitted; but it is requisite, if possible, to ascertain, whether the small change of capacity induced by temperature, is such as to *increase* the capacity, or to *diminish* it; and also, whether the increase or diminution is uniform or otherwise. Till this point is settled, it is of little use to mix water of 32° and 212°, with a view to obtain the true mean temperature.

That water *increases* in its capacity for heat with the increase of temperature, I consider demonstrable from the following arguments: 1st. A measure of water of any one temperature being mixed with a measure at any other temperature, the mixture is less than two measures. Now a condensation of volume is a certain mark of diminution of capacity and increase of temperature, whether the condensation be the effect of chemical agency, as in the mixture of sulphuric acid and water, or the effect of mechanical pressure, as with elastic fluids. 2. When the same body suddenly changes its capacity by a change of form, it is always from a *less* to a *greater*, as the temperature ascends; for instance, ice, water and vapor. 3. Dr. Crawford acknowledges from his own experience, that dilute sulphuric acid, and most other liquids he tried, were found to increase in their capacity for heat with the increase of temperature.

Admitting the force of these arguments, it follows that when water of 32° and 212° are mixed, and give a temperature denoted by 119° of the common thermometer, we must conclude that the true mean temperature is somewhere *below* that degree. I have already assigned the reasons why I place the mean at 110°.

With respect to the question whether water varies uniformly or otherwise in its capacity, I am inclined to think the increase, in this respect, will be found nearly proportional to the increase in bulk, and consequently will be four times as much at 212° as at the mean. Perhaps the expressions for the bulk may serve for the capacity; if so, the ratios of the capacities at 32°, 122° and 212° of the new scale, may be denoted by 22, 22$^1/_4$ and 23. I should rather expect, however, that the ratios are much nearer equality, and that 200, 201 and 204, would be nearer the truth.*

Dr. Crawford, when investigating the accuracy of the common thermometer, was aware, that if equal portions of water of different temperatures were mixed together, and the thermometer always indicated the mean, this was not an infallible proof of its accuracy. He allows that if water have an increasing capacity, and the mercury expand increasingly with the temperature, an equation may be formed so as to deceive us. This is in fact the case in some degree; and he appears to have been deceived by it. Yet the increased capacity of water, is by no means sufficient to balance the increased expansion of the mercury, as appears from the following experiments.

I took a vessel of tinned iron, the capacity of which was found to be equal to 2 oz. of water; into this were put 58 ounces of water, making the sum = 60 ounces of water. The whole was raised to any proposed temperature, and then two ounces of ice were put in and melted; the temperature was then observed, as follows:

60 oz. water of 212° + 2 oz. ice of 32°, gave 200$^1/_2$°
60 oz. water of 130° + 2 oz. ice of 32°, gave 122°
60 oz. water of 50° + 2 oz. ice of 32°, gave 45.3°

From the first of these, 30 parts of water lost 11$^1/_2$° each

* In the Lectures I delivered in Edinburgh and Glasgow in the spring of 1807, I gave it as my opinion that the capacity of water at 32° was to that at 212°, as 5 to 6, nearly. The opinion was founded on the fact I had just before observed, that a small mercurial thermometer at the temperature 32° being plunged into boiling water, rose to 202° in 15″; but the same at 212° being plunged into ice-cold water, was 18″ in descending to 42°; estimating the capacities to be reciprocally as the times of cooling, it gave the ratio of 5 to 6. On more mature consideration I am persuaded this difference is occasioned, not so much by the difference of capacities, as by the different degrees of fluidity. Water of 212° is more fluid than water of 32°, and distributes the temperature with greater facility. By a subsequent experiment too, I find, that mercury cools a thermometer twice as fast as water, though it has but half its capacity for heat; the times in which a thermometer is in cooling in fluids, are not, therefore, tests of their specific heats.

or 345°, and 1 part water of 32° gained 168°$1/2$; the difference 345—168$1/2$=176$1/2$°, expresses the number of degrees
of temperature (such as are found between 200 and 212 of
the old scale) entering into ice of 32° to convert it into
water of 32°. Similar calculations being made for the other
two, we find in the second, 150°, and in the third, 128°.
These three resulting numbers are nearly as 5, 6 and 7.
Hence it follows that as much heat is necessary to raise
water 5° in the lower part of the old scale, as is required to
raise it 7° in the higher, and 6° in the middle.*

Methods of finding the Specific Heats of Bodies.

The most obvious method of ascertaining the specific
heats of bodies that have no chemical affinity for water, is
to mix equal weights of water, and any proposed body of
two known temperatures, and to mark the temperature of
the mixture. Thus, if a pound of water of 32°, and a
pound of mercury of 212°, be mixed, and brought to a
common temperature, the water will be raised m degrees,
and the mercury depressed n degrees; and their capacities
or specific heats will be inversely as those numbers; or,
$n:m::$specific heat of water:specific heat of mercury. In this
way Black, Irvine, Crawford and Wilcke, approximated to
the capacities of various bodies. Such bodies as have an
affinity for water, may be confined in a vessel of known
capacity, and plunged into water so as to be heated or
cooled, as in the former case.

The results already obtained by this method are liable
to two objections: 1st. the authors presume the capacities
of bodies while they retain their form are permanent; that

* Perhaps the above results may account for the diversity in authors
respecting the quantity of *latent* heat (improperly so called) in water.
Respecting the doctrine of Black on Latent Heat, see an excellent note of
Leslie. (Inquiry, page 529.)

is, the specific heat increases exactly in proportion to the temperature; and 2d, that the common mercurial thermometer is a true test of temperature. But it has been shown that neither of these positions is warrantable.

The calorimeter of Lavoisier and Laplace was an ingenious contrivance for the purpose of investigating specific heat; it was calculated to show the quantity of ice which any body heated to a given temperature could melt. It was therefore not liable to the 2nd objection above. Unfortunately this instrument does not seem to have answered well in practice.

Meyer attempted to find the capacities of dried woods, by observing the times in which given equal volumes of them were in cooling. These times he considered as proportionate to the capacities bulk for bulk; and when the times were divided by the specific gravities, the quotient represented the capacities of equal weights. (Annal. de Chemie Tom. 30) . Leslie has since recommended a similar mode for liquids, and given us the results of his trials on 5 of them. From my own experience I am inclined to adopt this method as susceptible of great precision. The times in which bodies cool in like circumstances appear to be ascertainable this way with uncommon exactness, and as they are mostly very different, a very small error is of little consequence. The results too I find to agree with those by mixture; and they have the advantage of not being affected by any error in the thermometric scale.

The formulae for exhibiting the phenomena of the specific heats of bodies are best conceived from the contemplation of cylindrical vessels of unequal bases. (See plate 1. Fig. 1) . Supposing heat to be represented by a quantity of liquid in each vessel, and temperature by the height of the liquid in the vessel, the base denoting the zero or total privation of heat; then the specific heats of bodies at any given temperature, x, will be denoted by multiplying the area of the several bases by the height or temperature, x. Those specific heats too will be directly as the bases, or as the increments of heat necessary to produce equal changes of temperature.

Let w and W = the weights of two cold and hot bodies; c and C their capacities for heat at the same temperature (or the bases of the cylinders); d = the difference of the temperature of the two bodies before mixture, reckoned in degrees; m = the elevation of the colder body, and n = the depression of the warmer after mixture, (supposing them to have no chemical action); then we obtain the following equations.

$$1. \quad m + n = d.$$

$$2. \quad m = \frac{W\,C\,d}{w\,c + W\,C}.$$

$$3. \quad C = \frac{w\,c\,m}{W\,n}.$$

$$4. \quad c = \frac{W\,C\,n}{w\,m}.$$

If $C = c$, then, $\qquad 5. \quad m = \dfrac{W\,d}{W + w}.$

If $W = w$, then, $\qquad 6. \quad C = \dfrac{c\,m}{n}.$

To find the zero, or point of absolute privation of temperature, from observations on the change of capacity in the same body. Let c = the less, and C = the greater capacity, m = the number of degrees of the less capacity requisite to produce the change in equal weights, n = the number of degrees of the greater capacity, x = the whole number of degrees of temperature down to zero: then,

$$7. \quad C x - c x = C n = c m.$$

$$8. \quad x = \frac{C n}{C-c} = \frac{c m}{C-c}.$$

To find the zero from mixing two bodies of the same temperature which act chemically, and produce a change of temperature. Let w, W, c, C and x, be as before; let M = capacity of the mixture, and n = the degrees of heat or cold produced: then the quantity of heat in both bodies will be $= (c w + CW) x = (w + W) M x \pm (w + W) M n$.

$$9. \text{ and } x = \frac{(w + W) M n}{(c w + C W) \sim (w + W) M}.$$

It is to be regretted that so little improvement has been made for the last fifteen years in this department of science. Some of the earliest and most incorrect results are still obtruded upon the notice of students; though with the least reflection their errors are obvious. I have made a great number of experiments with a view to enlarge, but more especially, to correct the Tables of Specific Heat. It may be proper to relate some of the particulars. For liquids I used an egg-shaped thin glass vessel, capable of holding eight ounces of water; to this was adapted a cork, with a small circular hole, sufficient to admit the stem of a delicate ther-

mometer tube, which had two small marks with a file, the
one at 92°, and the other at 82°, both being above the
cork; when the cork was in the neck of the bottle, the bulb
of the thermometer was in the center of the internal capacity. When an experiment was made the bottle was filled
with the proposed liquid, and heated a little above 92°; it
was then suspended in the middle of a room, and the time
accurately noted when the thermometer was at 92°, and
again when it was 82°, another thermometer at the same
time indicating the temperature of the air in the room.
The capacity of the glass vessel was found = $^2/_3$ oz. of
water.

The mean results of several experiments were as
follows:

Air in the Room 52°

	Minutes.
Water cooled from 92° to 82°, in	29
Milk (1.026)	29
Solution of carbonate of potash (1.30)	$28^1/_2$
Solution of carbonate of ammonia (1.035)	$28^1/_2$
Ammoniacal solution (.948)	$28^1/_2$
Common vinegar (1.02)	$27^1/_2$
Solution of common salt, 88 W. + 32 S. (1.197)	27
Solution of soft sugar, 6 W. + 4 S. (1.17)	$26^1/_4$
Nitric acid (1.20)	$26^1/_2$
Nitric acid (1.30)	$25^1/_2$
Nitric acid (1.36)	25
Sulphuric acid (1.844) and water, equal bulks (1.535)	$23^1/_2$
Muriatic acid (1.153)	21
Acetic acid (1.056) from Acet. Cop.	21
Sulphuric acid (1.844)	$19^1/_2$
Alcohol (.85)	$19^1/_2$
Ditto (.817)	$17^1/_2$
Ether sulphuric (.76)	$15^1/_2$
Spermaceti oil (.87)	14

These times would express accurately the specific
heats of the several bodies, bulk for bulk, provided the
heat of the glass vessel did not enter into consideration.
But as the heat of that was proved to be equal to $^2/_3$ of an

ounce of water, or to $^4/_3$ of an ounce measure of oil, it is evident we must consider the heat disengaged in the 1st experiment, as from $8^2/_3$ ounces of water, and in the last as from $9^1/_3$ ounce measures of oil. On this account the numbers below 29 will require a small reduction, before they can be allowed to represent the times of cooling of *equal bulks* of the different liquids; in the last experiment the reduction will be one minute, and less in all the preceding ones.

It may be proper to observe, that the above results do not depend upon one trial of the several articles; most of the experiments were repeated several times, and the times of cooling were found not to differ more than half a minute; indeed, in general, there was no sensible differences. If the air in the room was, in any case, a little above or below 52°, the due allowance was made.

I found the specific heat of mercury, by mixture with water, and by the time of its cooling in a smaller vessel than the above, to be to that of water of equal bulk, as, .55 to 1 nearly.

I found the specific heats of the metals and other solids after the manner of Wilcke and Crawford; having procured a goblet, of very thin glass and small stem, I found its capacity for heat; then put water into it, such that the water, together with the value of the glass in water, might be equal to the weight of the solid. The solid was raised to 212°, and suddenly plunged into the water, and the specific heats of equal weights of the solid and the water, were inferred to be inversely as the changes of temperature which they experienced, according to the 6th formula. Some regard was paid to the correction, on account of the error of the common thermometer, which was used on the occasion. The solids I tried were iron, copper, lead, tin, zinc, antimony, nickel, glass, pitcoal, etc. The

TABLE OF SPECIFIC HEATS.

GASES.	equal weights	equal bulks
Hydrogen	21.40*	.002
Oxygen	4.75*	.006
Common air	1.79*	.002
Carbonic acid	1.05*	.002
Azotic	.79*	.001
Aqueous vapor	1.55*	.001

LIQUIDS.	equal weights	equal bulks
Water	1.00	1.00
Arterial blood	1.03*	
Milk (1.026)	.98	1.00
Carbonat. of ammon. (1.035)	.95	.98
Carbonat. of potash (1.30)	.75	.98
Solut. of ammonia (.948)	1.03	.98
Common vinegar (1.02)	.92	.94
Venous blood	.89*	
Solut. of common salt (1.197)	.78	.93
Solut. of sugar (1.17)	.77	.90
Nitric acid (1.20)	.76	.96
Nitric acid (1.30)	.68	.88
Nitric acid (1.36)	.63	.85
Nitrate of lime (1.40)	.62	.87
Sulph. acid and water, equal b.	.52	.80
Muriatic acid (1.153)	.60	.70
Acetic acid (1.056)	.66	.70
Sulphuric acid (1.844)	.35	.65
Alcohol (.85)	.76	.65
Ditto (.817)	.70	.57
Sulphuric ether (.76)	.66	.50
Spermaceti oil (.87)	.52	.45
Mercury	.04	.55

SOLIDS.	equal weights	equal bulks
Ice	.90?	.83
Dried woods, and other vegetable substances, from .45 to	.65	
Quicklime	.30	
Pit-coal (1.27)	.28	.36
Charcoal	26*	.67
Chalk	.27	
Hydrat. lime	.25	
Flint glass (2.87)	.19	
Muriate of soda	.23	.55
Sulphur	.19	
Iron	.13	1.00
Brass	.11	.97
Copper	.11	.98
Nickel	.10	.78
Zinc	.10	.69
Silver	.08	.84
Tin	.07	.51
Antimony	.06	.40
Gold	.05	.97
Lead	.04	.45
Bismuth	.04	.40

Oxides of the metals surpass the metals themselves, according to Crawford results differed little from those of Wilcke and Crawford; their numbers may, therefore, be adopted without any material error, till greater precision can be attained. In the following Table I have not carried the decimals beyond two places; because present experience will not warrant further extension: the first place of decimals may, I believe, be relied upon as accurate, and the second generally so, but in a few instances it may, perhaps, be 1 or 2 wrong; except from this observation, the specific heats of the gases by Crawford, on which I shall further remark.

Remarks on the Table.

The articles marked * are from Crawford. Notwithstanding the ingenuity and address displayed in his experiments on the capacities of the elastic fluids, there is reason to believe his results are not very near approximations to the truth; we can never expect accuracy when it depends upon the observation of 1 or 2 tenths of a degree of temperature after a tedious and complicated process. Great merit is undoubtedly due to him for the attempt. The difference between arterial and venous blood, on which he has founded the beautiful system of animal heat, is remarkable, and deserves further inquiry.

From the observed capacities of water, solution of ammonia, and the combustibles, into which hydrogen enters, together with its small specific gravity, we cannot doubt but that this element possesses a very superior specific heat. Oxygen, and azote likewise, undoubtedly stand high, as water and ammonia indicate; but the compound of these two elements denominated nitric acid, being so low, compared with the same joined to hydrogen, or water and ammonia, we must conclude that the superiority of the two last articles is chiefly due to the hydrogen they contain. The elements, charcoal and sulphur, are re-markably low, and carry their character along with them into compounds, as oil, sulphuric acid, etc.

Water appears to possess the greatest capacity for heat of any pure liquid yet known, whether it be compared with equal bulks or weights; indeed it may be doubted, whether any solid or liquid whatever contains more heat than an equal bulk of water of the same temperature. The great capacity of water arises from the strong affinity, which both its elements, hydrogen, and oxygen, have for heat. Hence it is that solutions of salts in water, contain generally less heat in a given volume than pure water: for, salts increase the volume of water as well as the density, and having mostly a small capacity for heat, they enlarge the volume of the water more than proportional to the heat they contribute.

Pure ammonia seems to possess a high specific heat, judging from the aqueous solution, which contains only about 10 per cent. If it could be exhibited pure in a liquid form, it would probably exceed water in this particular.

The compounds of hydrogren and carbon, under the characters of oil, ether and alcohol, and the woods, all fall below the two last mentioned; the reason seems to be, because charcoal is an element of a low specific heat.

The acids form an interesting class of bodies in regard to their specific heats. Lavoisier is the only one who is nearly correct in regard to nitric acid; he finds the specific heat of the acid 1.3 to be .66; this with some other of his results I find rather too low. It is remarkable that the water in acid of this strength is 63 per cent. and should have nearly as much heat in it as the compound is found to have, whence it should seem that the acid loses the principal part of its heat on combining with water. This is still more observable in muriatic acid, which contains 80 per cent. of water, and its specific heat is only .60; whence not only the heat of the acid gas, but part of that in the water is expelled on the union; this accounts for the great heat produced by the union of this acid gas with water.

The specific heat of sulphuric acid has been well approximated by several. Gadolin and Leslie make it .34, Lavoisier .33+; Crawford finds it .43, but he must probably have had a diluted acid.

Common vinegar, being water with 4 or 5 per cent. of acid, does not differ materially from water in its specific heat; it has been stated at .39 and at .10; but such results do not require animadversion. The acetic acid I used contained 33 per cent. pure acid; this acid therefore, in combining with water, expels much heat.

Quicklime is determined by Lavoisier and Crawford to be .22; I think they have underrated it: I find quicklime to impart as much or more heat than carbonate of lime, when inclosed in a vessel and plunged in water, or when mixed with oil. Hydrat of lime (that is, quicklime 3 parts and water 1 part, or dry slaked lime) is fixed at .28 by Gadolin: it was .25 by my first experiments; but I since find I have underrated it. The subject will be adverted to in a future section.

Theory of the Specific Heat of Elastic Fluids

Since the preceding section was printed off, I have spent some time in considering the constitution of elastic fluids with regard to heat. The results already obtained cannot be relied upon; yet it is difficult to conceive and execute experiments less exceptionable than those of Crawford. It is extremely important, however, to obtain the exact specific heat of elastic fluids, because the phenomena of combustion and of heat in general, and consequently a great part of chemical agency, are intimately connected therewith.

In speaking of the uncertainty of Crawford's results on the specific heat of elastic fluids, it must not be understood that *all* of them are equally implicated. The reiterated experiments on the heat given out by the combustion of hydrogen, in which it was found that 11 measures of mixed gases, when fired by electricity heated 20.5 measures of water 2.4° (page 263) at a medium, were susceptible of very considerable accuracy, and are therefore entitled to credit. The comparative heat of atmosphere air and water, which rested on the observance of nearly ¼ of a degree of temperature, is probably not very far from the truth; but the very small differences in the heats communicated by equal bulks of oxygen, hydrogen, carbonic acid, azotic gas and common air, together with the great importance of those differences in the calculation, render the results very uncertain. He justly observes, that if we suppose the heats imparted by equal bulks of these gases to be equal, it will not affect his doctrine. The tenor of it necessarily led him to estimate the heat of oxygen high, compared with equal weights of carbonic acid and aqueous vapor, and of azotic gas or *phlogisticated* air, as it was then called, under the idea of its being an opposite to oxygen or *dephlogisticated* air. Indeed his deductions respecting azotic gas, are not consistent with his experiments: for he makes no use of experiments 12 and 13, which are the only direct ones for the purpose, but he infers the heat of azotic gas from the observed difference between oxygen and common air. The result gives it less than half that of common air; whereas from the 13th experiment, scarcely any sensible difference was perceived between them. He has in all probability much underrated it; but his errors in this respect whatever they may be, do not affect his system.

When we consider that all elastic fluids are equally expanded by temperature, and that liquids and solids are not so, it should seem that a general law for the affection of elastic fluids for heat, ought to be more easily deducible and more simple than one for liquids, or solids. There are three suppositions in regard to elastic fluids which merit discussion.

1. *Equal weights of elastic fluids may have the same quantity of heat under like circumstances of temperature and pressure.*

The truth of this supposition is disproved by several facts: oxygen and hydrogen upon their union give out much heat, though they form steam, an elastic fluid of the same weight as the elements composing it. Nitrous gas and oxygen unite under similar circumstances. Carbonic acid is formed by the union of charcoal, a substance of low specific heat, with oxygen; much heat is given out, which must be principally derived from the oxygen; if then the charcoal contain little heat, and the oxygen combining with it be reduced, the carbonic acid must be far inferior in heat to an equal weight of oxygenous gas.

2. *Equal bulks of elastic fluids may have the same quantity of heat with the same pressure and temperature.*

This appears much more plausible; the diminution of volume when a mixture of oxygen and hydrogen is converted into steam, may be occasioned by a proportionate diminution of the absolute heat; the same may be said of a mixture of nitrous gas and oxygen. The minute differences observed by Crawford, may have been inaccuracies occasioned by the complexity of his experiments. But there are other considerations which render this supposition extremely improbable, if they do not altogether disprove it. Carbonic acid contains its own bulk of oxygen; the heat given out at its formation must therefore be exactly equal to the whole heat previously contained in the charcoal on this supposition; but the heat by the combustion of one pound of charcoal seems, at least, equal to the heat by the combustion of a quantity of hydrogen sufficient to produce one pound of water, and this last is equal to, or more than the heat retained by the water, because steam is nearly twice the density of the elastic mixture from which it is produced; it should therefore follow, that charcoal should be found of the same specific heat as water, whereas it is only about $1/4$ of it. Were this supposition true, the specific heats of elastic fluids of equal weights would be inversely as their specific gravities. If that of steam or aqueous vapor were represented by 1, oxygen would be .64, hydrogen 8.4, azote .72, and carbonic acid .46. But the supposition is untenable.

3. *The quantity of heat belonging to the ultimate particles of all elastic fluids, must be the same under the same pressure and temperature.*

It is evident the number of ultimate particles or molecules in a given weight or volume of one gas is not the same as in another: for, if equal measures of azotic and oxygenous gases were mixed, and could be instantly united chemically, they would form nearly two measures of nitrous gas, having the same weight as the two original measures; but the number of ultimate particles could at most be one half of that before the union. No two elastic fluids, probably, therefore, have the same number of particles, either in the same volume or the same weight. Suppose, then, a given volume of any elastic fluid to be constituted of particles, each surrounded with an atmosphere of heat repelling each other through the medium of those atmospheres, and in a state of equilibrium under the pressure of a constant force, such as the earth's atmosphere, also at the temperature of the surrounding bodies; suppose further, that by some sudden change each molecule of air was endued with a stronger affinity for heat; query the change that would take place in consequence of this last supposition. The only answer that can be given, as it appears to me, is this. The particles will condense their respective atmospheres of heat, by which their mutual repulsion will be diminished, and the external pressure will therefore effect a proportionate condensation in the volume of air: neither an increase nor diminution in the quantity of heat around each molecule, or around the whole, will take place. Hence the truth of the supposition, or as it may now be called, proposition, is demonstrated.

Corol. 1. The specific heats of equal *weights* of any two elastic fluids, are inversely as the weights of their atoms or molecules.

2. The specific heats of equal *bulks* of elastic fluids, are directly as their specific gravities, and inversely as the weights of their atoms.

3. Those elastic fluids that have their atoms the most condensed, have the strongest attraction for heat; the greater attraction is spent in accumulating more heat in a given space or volume, but does not increase the quantity around any single atom.

4. When two elastic atoms unite by chemical affinity to form one elastic atom, one half of their heat is disengaged. When three unite, then two thirds of their heat is disengaged, etc. And in general, when m elastic particles by chemical union become n; the heat given out is to the heat retained as $m-n$ is to n.

One objection to this proposition it may be proper to obviate: it will be said, an increase in the specific attraction of each atom must produce the same effect on the system as an increase of external pressure. Now this last is known to express or give out a quantity of the absolute heat; therefore the former must do the same. This conclusion must be admitted; and it tends to establish the truth of the preceding proposition. The heat expressed by doubling the density of any elastic fluid amounts to about 50°, according to my former experiments; this heat is not so much as one hundreth part of the whole, as will be shown hereafter, and therefore does not materially affect the specific heat: it seems to be merely the interstitial heat amongst the small globular molecules of air, and scarcely can be said to belong to them, because it is equally found in a vacuum or space devoid of air, as is proved by the increase of temperature upon admitting air into a vacuum.

Before we can apply this doctrine to find the specific heat of elastic fluids, we must first ascertain the relative weights of their ultimate particles. Assuming at present what will be proved hereafter, that if the weight of an atom of hydrogen be 1, that of oxygen will be 7, azote 5, nitrous gas 12, nitrous oxide 17, carbonic acid 19, ammoniacal gas 6, carburetted hydrogen 7, olefiant gas 6, nitric acid 19, carbonic oxide 12, sulphuretted hydrogen 16, muriatic acid 22, aqueous vapor 8, ethereal vapor 11, and alcoholic vapor 16; we shall have the specific heats of the several elastic fluids as in the following table. In order to compare them with that of water, we shall further assume the specific heat of water to that of steam as 6 to 7, or as 1 to 1.166.

TABLE OF THE SPECIFIC HEATS OF ELASTIC FLUIDS.

Hydrogen	9.382	Olefiant gas	1.555
Azote	1.866	Nitric acid	.491
Oxygen	1.333	Carbonic oxide	.777
Atmos. air	1.759	Sulph. hydrogen	.583
Nitrous gas	.777	Muriatic acid	.424
Nitrous oxide	.549	Aqueous vapor	1.166
Carbonic acid	.491	Ether. vapor	.848
Ammon. gas	1.555	Alcohol. vapor	.586
Carb. hydrogen	1.333	Water	1.000

Let us now see how far these results will accord with experience. It is remarkable that the heat of common air comes out nearly the same as Crawford found it by experiment; also, hydrogen excells all the rest as he determined; but oxygen is much lower and azote higher. The principles of Crawford's doctrine of animal heat and combustion, however, are not at all affected with the change. Besides the reason already assigned for thinking that azote has been rated too low, we see from the Table, page 50, that ammonia, a compound of hydrogen and azote, has a higher specific heat than water, a similar compound of hydrogen and oxygen.

Upon the whole, there is not any established fact in regard to the specific heats of bodies, whether elastic or liquid, that is repugnant to the above table as far as I know; and it is to be hoped, that some principle analogous to the one here adopted, may soon be extended to solid and liquid bodies in general.

On the Quantity of Heat Evolved by

Combustion

When certain bodies unite chemically with oxygen, the process is denominated *combustion,* and is generally accompanied with the evolution of heat, in consequence of the diminished capacities of the products. The fine attempt of Lavoisier and Laplace to find the quantities of heat disengaged during different species of combustion, has not been followed up with the attention it deserves. Perhaps this may have been owing to the supposed necessity of using the calorimeter of the above philosophers, and to a notion that its results are not always to be depended upon. Much important information may, however, be obtained on this subject by the use of a very simple apparatus, as will appear from what follows:

I took a bladder, the bulk of which, when extended with air, was equal to 30000 grains of water; this was filled with any combustible gas, and a pipe and stop-cock adapted to it: a tinned vessel, capable of containing 30000 grains of water was provided, and its capacity for heat being found, so much water was put into it as to make the vessel and water together, equal to 30000 grains of water. The gas was lighted, and the point of the small flame was applied to the concavity of the bottom of the tinned vessel, till the whole of the gas was consumed; the increase of the temperature of the water was then carefully noted; whence the effect of the combustion of a given volume of gas, of the common pressure and temperature, in raising the temperature of an equal volume of water, was ascertained, except a very small loss of heat by radiation, etc. which this method must be liable to, and which probably does not exceed $1/_8$ or $1/_{10}$th of the whole.

Hydrogen, combustion of it raises an equal
   volume of water   4.5°
Coal gas, or carburetted hydrogen 10.—
Olefiant tgas   14
Carbonic oxide   4.5

Oil, alcohol, and ether, were burned in a lamp, etc. and the effect observed as under:

Oil, spermaceti, combustion of 10 grs. raised
   30000 grs. water   5°
—of turpentine (much smoke unburnt) 3
Alcohol (.817)   2.9
Ether, sulphuric   3.1
Tallow and wax   5.2
Phosphor.—10 grs. heated 30000 grs. water 3
Charcoal   2
Sulphur   1
Camphor   3.5
Caoutchouc   2.1

The mean results of several trials of the different gases are stated above; when the experiments are performed with due care, there is scarcely any sensible difference in the results with the same species of gas. The point of the flame should just touch the bottom of the vessel.

The five last articles were placed upon a convenient stand, and burned under the vessel of water; except charcoal, a piece of which was ignited, then weighed, and the combustion was maintained by a gentle blast from a blowpipe, directing the heat as much as possible upon the bottom of the vessel; after the operation it was again weighed, and the loss ascertained; the result never amounted to 2° for ten grains, but generally approached it nearly.

In order to exhibit the comparative effects more clearly, it may be proper to reduce the articles to a common weight, and to place along with them the quantity of oxygen known to combine with them. The quantity of heat given out may well be expressed by the number of pounds of ice which it would melt, taking it for granted that the quantity necessary to melt ice, is equal to that which would raise water 150° of the new scale. The results may be seen in the following table.

1 lb. hydrogen takes	7 lbs. oxygen, produces	8 lbs. water, melts	320 lbs. ice.
—— carbur. hydrogen	4 —— ——	5 w. and car. acid	85 ——
—— olefiant gas	3.5 —— ——	4.5 ——	88 ——
—— carbonic oxide	.58 —— ——	1.58 carb. acid	25 ——
—— oil, wax and tal.	3.5 —— ——	4.5 w. and car. acid	104 ——
—— oil of turp.	— —— ——	— ——	60 ——
—— alcohol	— —— ——	— ——	58 ——
—— ether	3 —— ——	4 ——	62 ——
—— phosphorus	1.5 —— ——	2.5 phos. acid	60 ——
—— charcoal	2.8 —— ——	3.8 carb. acid	40 ——
—— sulphur	— —— ——	— sulph. acid	20 ——
—— camphor	— —— ——	— w. and car. acid	70 ——
—— caouchouc	— —— ——	— ——	42 ——

Lavoisier has left us a similar table derived from experiments on the calorimeter, for hydrogen, phosphorus, charcoal, oil and wax; and Crawford for hydrogen, charcoal, oil and wax, derived from their combustion in another apparatus. By reducing Crawford's results to a comparative scale with Lavoisier's, they will both appear as follows:

	according to Lavoisier.	according to Crawford.
1 lb. Hydrogen by combustion melts	295 lbs. ice	480 lbs. ice.
— Phosphorus ———	100 —	— —
— Charcoal ———	96.5 —	69 —
— Wax ———	133 —	97 —
— Oil ———	148 —	89 —

HYDROGEN. The near coincidence of Lavoisier's result and mine is an argument in favor of their accuracy. Crawford, I think, must have overrated the heat produced; his method of determining it, by the explosion of the gases by electricity, seems however susceptible of precision, and ought to be repeated. The truth perhaps lies between the two.

PHOSPHORUS. Lavoisier's result, which is much greater than mine, must, I think, be too high. I suspect that 66 is as much as can be fairly inferred.

CHARCOAL. The inferiority of my results to those of Crawford is what might be expected. Mine must necessarily be rather too low. But Lavoisier is in this as well as all the other articles, hydrogen excepted, unwarrantably too high. I think Crawford will be found too high; his experiments on the heat produced by the respiration of animals, support this supposition.

WAX AND OIL. Crawford's results are a little lower than mine, which they ought not to be, and are doubtless below the truth. Lavoisier's certainly cannot be supported. This great philosopher was well aware of the uncertainty of his results, and expresses himself accordingly. He seems not to have had an adequate idea of the heat of hydrogen gas, which contributes so much to the quantity given out by its combustion; he compares, and expects to find an equation, between the heat given out by burning wax, etc. and the heat given out by the combustion of equal weights of hydrogen and charcoal in their separate state; but this cannot be expected, as both hydrogen and charcoal in a state of combination must contain less heat than when separate, agreeably to the general law of the evolution of heat on combination. In fact, both Crawford and Lavoisier have been, in some degree, led away by the notion, that oxygenous gas was the sole or principal source of the light and heat produced by combustion. This is the more remarkable of the former, after he had proved that hydrogenous gas, one of the most frequent and abundant combustibles, possessed nearly five times as much heat as the same weight of oxygenous gas. Azote, another combustible, possesses as high and probably higher specific heat than oxygen. Oil, wax, tallow, alcohol, etc. would be far from being low in the table of specific heat, provided a table were formed comprehending bodies of every class. Charcoal and sulphur rank but low in the table. Upon the whole then, we cannot adopt the language of Crawford, "that inflammable bodies contain little absolute heat," and "that the heat which is produced by combustion is derived from the air, and not from the inflammable body." This language may be nearly right as applied to the ordinary combustion of charcoal and pitcoal; but cannot be so when applied universally to combustible bodies.

After these remarks it is almost unnecessary to add that the heat, and probably the light also, evolved by combustion, must be conceived to be derived both from the oxygen and the combustible body; and that each contributes, for aught we know to the contrary, in proportion to its specific heat before the combustion. A similar observation may be made upon the heat produced by the union of sulphur with the metals, and every other chemical union in which heat is evolved.

Before we conclude this section it may be proper to add, for the sake of those who are more immediately interested in the economy of fuel, that the heat given out by the combustion of 1 lb. of charcoal, and perhaps also of pitcoal, is sufficient (if there were no loss) to raise 45 or 50 lbs. of water from the freezing to the boiling temperature; or it is sufficient to convert 7 or 8 lbs. of water into steam. If more than this weight of coal be used, there is a proportionate quantity of heat lost, which ought, if possible, to be avoided.

On the Natural Zero of Temperature

Or absolute Privation of Heat.

If we suppose a body at the ordinary temperature to contain a given quantity of heat, like as a vessel contains a given quantity of water, it is plain that by abstracting successively small equal portions, the body would finally be exhausted of the fluid. It is an object of primary importance in the doctrine of heat to determine, how many degrees of the ordinary scale of temperature a body must be depressed before it would lose all its heat, or become absolutely cold. We have no means of effecting this by direct experiment; but we can acquire data for a calculus, from which the zero may be approximated with considerable accuracy.

The data requisite for the calculus are the exact specific heats of the several bodies operated upon, and the quantity of heat evolved, or absorbed by bodies, in cases of their chemical combinations or otherwise. These data are not to be acquired without great care and circumspection; and hence the great diversity of the results hitherto obtained in this difficult investigation. According to some, the zero is estimated to be 900° below the common temperature; while, according to others, it is nearly 8000° below the same. These are the extremes; but various determinations of an intermediate nature are to be found.

The most simple case in theory is that of ice and water: supposing the capacities of these two bodies to be as 9 to 10, at the temperature of 32°, it is known that ice of 32° requires as much heat as would raise water 150°, to convert it into water of 32°, or to melt it. Consequently, according to the 8th formula, page 47, water of 32°, must contain 10 times as much heat, or 1500°. That is, the zero must be placed at 1500° below the temperature of freezing water. Unfortunately, however, the capacity of ice has not been determined with sufficient accuracy, partly because of its being a solid of a bad conducting power, but principally because the degrees of the common thermometer below freezing, are very erroneous from the equal division of the scale.

Besides the one already mentioned, the principal subjects that have been used in this investigation are, 1st, mixtures of sulphuric acid and water; 2d, mixtures of lime and water; 3d, mixture or combination of nitric acid and lime; and 4th, combustion of hydrogen, phosphorus and charcoal. Upon these it will be necessary to enlarge.

Mixture of Sulphuric Acid and Water.

According to the experiments of Lavoisier and Laplace on the calorimeter, a mixture of sulphuric acid and water in the proportion of 4 to 3 by weight, determines the zero at 7292° below freezing water, reckoning by Fahrenheit. But a mixture of 4 acid with 5 water, determines the same at 2630°.

Gadolin made several experiments on mixtures of sulphuric acid and water, the results of which are as accurate as can be expected in a first essay of the kind. He has not determined the zero from his experiments, but taking it for granted to be 1400° below the freezing point on the supposition that the capacities of ice and water are as 9 to 10, he has inquired how far his experiments corroborate the same, by comparing the capacities of the mixtures by experiment with those calculated from the previous assumption. His results are thus curtailed in their utility; but as he has given us data sufficient to calculate the zero from each experiment, it will be proper to see how far they accord with Lavoisier's, or those of others.

Taking the specific heat of water at 1, Gadolin finds, by direct experiment, the specific heat of concentrated sulphuric acid to be .339 (See Crawford on heat, page 465); he then mixes the acid and water in various proportions, observes the increase of temperature, and then finds the capacities of the mixtures. Whence we have data to find the zero by formula 9, page 47. In giving his numbers, I have changed his scale, the centigrade, to Fahrenheit's.

Acid		Water	heat evolv.	capa. of mix.	comp. zero
4	+	1	194°	.442	2936°
2	+	1	203	.500	1710
1	+	1	161	.605	1510
1	+	2	108	.749	2637
1	+	5	51	.876	3230
1	+	10	28	.925	1740

The mean of these is 2300°, which is far beyond what Gadolin supposes to be the zero, as deduced from the relative capacities of ice and water, and to which he seeks to accommodate these experiments.

As the heat evolved upon the mixture of sulphuric acid and water is so considerable, and as all three articles are liquids, and consequently admit of having their capacities ascertained with greater precision, I have long been occasionally pursuing the investigation of the zero from experiments on these liquids. The strongest sulphuric acid of 1.855, I find has the specific heat .33, and

Acid		Water	sp. gr.	heat evol.	capa. of mix.	zero
5.77	+	1	(1.78)	160°	.420	6400°
1.6	+	1	(1.520)	260	.553	4150
1	+	2	(1.250)	100	.764	6000

I reject all mixtures where the heat is less than 100°, because the difference between the observed capacity of the mixture, and the mean capacity is too small to be determined with precision. These results differ materially from Gadolin's. I believe they will be found to be nearer approximations to the truth. When the two liquids are mixed in nearly equal weights, the results give the zero less remote than otherwise; this appears to be the case both with Gadolin and me; I have not yet been able to discover the cause of it; perhaps the capacity of such mixture increases with the temperature more than in the other cases.

Lime and Water.

Quicklime, that is, lime recently burned, has a strong affinity for water; when mixed in due proportion an intense heat is produced; the lime falls, or becomes slaked, and then may be denominated hydrat of lime. If no more water is put to quicklime than is sufficient to slake it, or pulverize it, three parts of lime, by weight, form four parts of hydrat, a perfectly dry powder, from which the water cannot be expelled under a red heat. If more water is added, the mixture forms mortar, a pasty compound, from which the excess of water may be expelled by a boiling heat, and the hydrat remains a dry powder. When hydrat of lime and water are mixed, no heat is evolved; hence the two form a mere mixture, and not a chemical compound. The heat then which is evolved in slaking lime, arises from the chemical union of three parts of lime and one of water, or from the formation of the hydrat, and any excess of water diminishes the sensible heat produced. Before any use can be made of these facts for determining the zero, it becomes necessary to determine the specific heat of dry hydrat of lime. For this purpose a given weight of lime is to be slaked with an excess of water; the excess must then be expelled by heat till the hydrat is $1/_3$ heavier than the lime. A given weight of this powder may then be mixed with the same, or any other weight of water of another temperature, and its specific heat determined accordingly. By a variety of experiments made in this way, and with sundry variations, I find the specific heat of hydrat of lime about .40, and not .25 as in the table, page 50. Lime itself I find to be nearly .30. Crawford undervalues lime, by mixing cold lime with hot alcohol; the lime does not produce a sufficient effect on the alcohol, because it contains water, which acts upon the lime. I have no doubt a different specific heat would have been found, if cold alcohol had been poured on hot lime. The heat evolved in the formation of hydrat of lime may be found as follows: If 1 oz. of lime be put into 4 oz. of water, the temperature of the mixture will be raised 100°; in this case $1^1/_3$ oz. hydrat is formed, and the heat evolved raises it together with $3^2/_3$ oz. water 100°; but $3^2/_3$ water contains 7 times the heat that $1^1/_3$ hydrat of lime does; therefore the heat given out is sufficient to raise 8 times the hydrat 100°, or once the hydrat 800°. Whence the heat evolved by mixing 3 parts of lime and 1 of water, is sufficient to raise the new compound 800°. Applying then the theorem in page 47, we obtain the zero = 4260° below the common temperature.

Nitric Acid and Lime.

According to the experiments of Lavoisier and Laplace, the specific heat of nitric acid, sp. gr. 1.3, is .661, and that of lime .217, and a compound of $9^{1}/_{3}$ parts of said acid, and one of lime, is .619. But supposing there was no change of capacity upon combination, this compound should only have the capacity .618; whereas, in fact, the mixture produces an increase of temperature of about 180°, and therefore ought to be found with a diminished capacity, or one below .618. Were this fact to be established, it would exhibit an inexplicable phenomenon, unless to those who adopt the notion of *free* caloric and *combined* caloric existing in the same body, or to speak more properly, of caloric combined so as to retain all its characteristic properties, and caloric combined so as to lose the whole of them. One error in this statement has already been pointed out, in regard to the capacity of lime. If we adopt the specific heat of lime to be .30, and apply the theorem for the zero, we shall find it to be 15770° below the common temperature, as deduced from the above data so corrected.

I took a specimen of nitric acid of the specific gravity 1.2, and found, by repeated trials, its specific heat to be .76 by weight. Into 4600 grains of this acid of 35° temperature, in a thin flask, 657 grains of lime were gradually dropped, and the mixture moderately agitated; in one or two minutes after $^{3}/_{4}$ths of the lime was in and dissolved, the thermometer rose nearly to 212°, and the mixture was beginning to boil; it was suffered to cool 20°, when the rest of the lime was added, and it again rose to the boiling point; about 15 grains of insoluble residuum were left. These were taken out, and their place supplied by 15 grains of fresh lime, which were dissolved, and left a clear liquid nearly saturated, of 1.334 sp. gravity. The specific heat of this was found to be .69. The increase of temperature being called 200°, and the specific heat of lime being .30, we find the zero to be 11000° below the freezing temperature. The experiment was varied by taking acids of different strengths, and various proportions of lime, but the results still gave the zero more remote than either of the previous methods. Perhaps the reason may be that lime is still underrated.

Combustion of Hydrogen.

Lavoisier finds the combustion of 1 lb. of hydrogen to melt 295 lbs. of ice. The results of my experience give 320 lbs., and Crawford's 480. Till this fact can be more accurately ascertained, we may take 400 lbs. as approximating to the truth. Or, which amounts to the same thing, the combustion of 1 lb. of hydrogen takes 7 lbs. of oxygen, and gives out heat which would raise 8 lbs. of water 7500°. By adopting Crawford's capacities of hydrogen and oxygen, and applying the theorem, page 47, we find the zero 1290° from the common temperature. But if we adopt the preceding theory of the specific heat of elastic fluids, and apply the 4th corol. page 58, we must conclude that in the formation of steam, one half of the whole heat of both its elements is given out; the conversion of 8 lbs. of steam into water, will give out heat sufficient to melt 56 lbs. of ice; therefore one half of the whole heat in 1 lb. of hydrogen, and 7 lbs. of oxygen together, or which is the same thing, the whole heat in 1 lb. of hydrogen, or 7 lbs. of oxygen separately, will melt 344 lbs. of ice; now if from 688 we take 400, there remain 288 for the lbs. of ice, which the heat in 8 lbs. of water, at the ordinary temperature, is sufficient to melt, or the heat in 1 lb. is capable of melting 36 lbs. of ice: hence the zero will be 5400° below freezing water.

Combustion of Phosphorus.

One pound of phosphorus requires $1^1/_2$ lb. of oxygen, and melts 66 lbs. of ice. The specific heat of phosphorus is not known; but from analogy one may suppose it to have as much heat as oil, wax, tallow, etc. which is nearly half as much as water. From the last article it seems, that the whole heat in each lb. of oxygen is sufficient to melt 50 lbs. of ice; whence the whole heat in both articles, previous to combustion, is sufficient to melt $75 + 18 = 93$ lbs. of ice. From which deducting 66, there remains 27 for the pounds of ice, which the heat in 2.5 lbs. of phosphoric acid ought to melt. This would give the specific heat of that acid .30, a supposition not at all improbable. The result of the combustion of phosphorus seems then to corroborate that from hydrogen.

Combustion of Charcoal.

Crawford's data are, specific heat of charcoal .26, oxygen 4.749, carbonic acid 1.0454, and the heat given out by burning 1 lb. of charcoal = 69 lbs. ice = 10350°. It is now established beyond doubt, that 1 lb. of charcoal requires 2.6 lbs. of oxygen to convert it into carbonic acid. From these data, by the theorem, page 47, we deduce the zero = 4400°. But Crawford himself has not noticed this deduction. If we adopt the theory of specific heat, and the table founded on it, combined with the supposition of the zero being 6000° below the common temperature, (see page 59) we shall have from the general formula, this equation,

$$\frac{(1+2.6) \times .491 \times h}{1 \times .26 + 2.6 \times 1.333 - 3.6 \times .491} = 6000°$$

where h represents the degrees of temperature which the combustion of 1 lb. of charcoal would raise the product, or 3.6 lbs. of carbonic acid. From this, h is found $= 6650°$. But this heat would raise 3.6 lbs. of water $= 6650 \times .4491 = 3265°$. Or it would raise 1 lb. of water, 11750°; or it would melt 78 lbs. of ice. Lavoisier finds the effect $= 96$ lbs. and Crawford finds it $= 69$. So that the supposed distance of the zero is not discountenanced by the combustion of charcoal, as far as the theory is concerned.

Combustion of Oil, Wax and Tallow.

We do not know the exact constitution of these compounds, nor the quantity of oxygen which they require; but from the experiments of Lavoisier, as well as from some attempts of my own, I am inclined to think, that they are formed of about 5 parts of charcoal and 1 of hydrogen by weight, and that 6 parts require 21 of oxygen for their combustion, forming 19 parts of carbonic acid and 8 of water. Let it be supposed that the zero is 6900° below freezing water, or that the heat in water of 32°, is sufficient to melt 46 lbs. of ice, then the heat in steam will be sufficient to melt 53 lbs. By applying Cor. 1, at page 58, we shall find the heat in oxygenous gas $= 60.5$ lbs. and in carbonic acid, 22.3 lbs. The heat in 1 lb. of oil, etc. equal to half that of water $= 23$ lbs. which being added to 211.7, the heat in 3.5 lbs. of oxygen, gives 234.7 lbs. of ice, which would be melted by all the heat in 1 lb. of oil and 3.5 of oxygen; but the products of combustion are 1.3 lb. of water, and 3.2 lbs. of carbonic acid, together containing as much heat as would melt 131.2 lbs. of ice; this being subtracted from 234.7, leaves 103.5 for the ice to be melted by the heat evolved during the combustion of 1 lb. of oil, wax or tallow, which agrees with the experiment. The conclusion then supports the supposition, that the zero is 6900° below freezing water.

Combustion of Ether, etc.

I have pretty accurately ascertained the products of the combustion of 1 lb. of ether to be 1.75 water, and 2.25 carbonic acid, derived from its union with 3 lbs. of oxygen. By instituting a calculation similar to the above, but on the supposition of the zero being 6000° below freezing water, I find the heat given out on the combustion of ether, ought to be = 67 lbs. of ice: it was observed to be 62, and the difference may well be attributed to the loss unavoidable in my method of observation.

I might here inquire into the results of the combustion of the other articles mentioned in the table, page 63, as far as they affect the present question; but I consider those above noticed as the most to be depended upon. From the result of olefiant gas we may learn, that a combustible body in the gaseous state, does not give out much more heat than when in a liquid state; for, oil and olefiant gas certainly do not differ much in their constitution; one would therefore have expected the same weight of olefiant gas to have yielded more heat than oil, because of the heat required to maintain the elastic state; but it should seem that the heat requisite to convert a liquid to an elastic fluid, is but a small portion of the whole, a conclusion evidently countenanced by the experiments and observations contained in the preceding pages.

It may be proper now to draw up the results of my experience, reported in the present section, into one point of view.

	Zero below 32° Fahrenheit.
From a mixture of 5.77 sulphuric acid and 1 water	6400°
—————————— 1.6 ——————————1 ——	4150
—————————— 1 ——————————2 ——	6000
—————————— 3 lime 1 ——	4260
—————————— 7 nitric acid 1 lime	11000
From the combustion of hydrogen	5400
——————————— phosphorus	5400
——————————— charcoal	6000
——————————— oil, wax and tallow	6900
——————————— ether	6000

The mean of all these is 6150°. We are authorized then, till something more decisive appear, to consider the natural zero of temperature as being about 6000° below the temperature of freezing water, according to the divisions of Fahrenheit's scale. The differences of the above results are not greater than what may be ascribed to inaccuracies, except the 2d and 5th. I believe it will be impossible to reconcile these two to each other, unless it is upon the supposition of a change of capacity with change of temperature in one or both of the mixtures. This deserves farther inquiry.

Heat produced by Percussion and Friction

The heat produced by the percussion and friction of solid bodies, arises from one and the same cause, namely, from a condensation of volume, and consequent diminution of capacity of the excited body; exactly in the same manner as the condensation of air produces heat. It is a well known fact, that iron and other metals, by being hammered, become hot and condensed in volume at the same time; and if a diminution of capacity has not been observed it is because it is small, and has not been investigated with sufficient accuracy. That a change of capacity actually takes place cannot be doubted, when it is considered, that a piece of iron once hammered in this way, is unfitted for a repetition of the effect, till it has been heated in a fire and cooled gradually. Count Rumford has furnished us with some important facts on the production of heat by friction. He found that in boring a cannon for 30 minutes, the temperature was raised 70°; and that it suffered a loss of 837 grains by the dust, and scales torn off, which amounted to $1/_{948}$ part of the cylinder. *On the supposition that all the heat was given out by these scales,* he finds they must have lost 66360° of temperature; when at the same time he found their specific heat not sensibly diminished. But this is manifestly an incorrect view of the subject: the heat excited does not arise from the scales merely, else how should hammering make a body red hot without any loss of scales? The fact is, the whole mass of metal is more or less condensed by the violence used in boring, and a rise of temperature of 70 or 100° is too small to produce a sensible diminution in its capacity for heat. Does Count Rumford suppose, that if in this case the quantity of metal operated upon had been 1 lb. and the dust produced the same as above, that the whole quantity of heat evolved would have been the same?

The phenomena of heat produced by friction and percussion, however, sufficiently show that the zero of temperature cannot be placed at so small a distance as 1000° or 1500° below the common temperature, as has been determined by some philosophers.

Section 7

On the Motion and Communication of Heat,

Arising from inequality of Temperature.

As from various sources the temperature of bodies is liable to perpetual fluctuation, it becomes of importance to determine the nature of the motion of heat in the same body, and in its passage from one body to another, arising from its incessant tendency to an equilibrium.

A solid bar being heated at one end, and exposed to the air, the heat is partly dissipated in the air, and partly conducted along the bar, exhibiting a gradation of temperature from the hot to the cold end. This power of conducting heat varies greatly, according to the nature of the subject: in general, metals, and those bodies which are good conductors of electricity, are likewise good conductors of heat; and *vice versa.*

When a fluid is heated at its surface, the heat gradually and slowly descends in the same manner as along a solid; and fluids seem to have a difference in their conducting power analogous to that of solids. But when the heat is applied to the bottom of a vessel, containing a fluid, the case is very different; the heated particles of the fluid, in consequence of their diminished specific gravity, form an ascending current and rise to the surface, communicating a portion of heat in their ascent to the contiguous particles, but still retaining a superiority of temperature; so that the increase of temperature in the mass is first observed at the surface, and is constantly greatest there till the commencement of ebullition in liquids, at which period the temperature is uniform. The conducting power of fluids then arises from two distinct sources; the one is the same as in solids, namely, a gradual progress of the heat from particle to particle, exclusive of any motion of the particles themselves; the other arises from the internal motion of the particles of the fluid, by which the extremes of hot and cold are perpetually brought into contact, and the heat is thus diffused with great celerity. The latter source is so much more effectual than the former, that some have been led, though without sufficient reason, to doubt the existence of the former, or that fluids do convey heat in the same manner as solids.

Nothing appears, then, but that the communication of heat from particle to particle, is performed in the same way in fluids as in solids; the rapidity of its diffusion in fluids, is to be ascribed to an hydrostatical law. But there is another method by which heat is propagated through a vacuum, and through elastic fluids, which demands our particular notice. By this we receive the heat of the sun; and by this, when in a room, we receive the heat of an ordinary fire. It is called the *radiation* of heat; and the heat so propelled, is called *radiant heat*.

Till lately we have been used to consider the light and heat of the sun as the same thing. But Dr. Herschel has shown, that there are rays of heat proceeding from the sun, which are separable by a prism from the rays of light; they are subject to reflection, like light; and to refraction, but in a less degree, which is the cause of their separability from light. The velocity of radiant heat is not known; but it may be presumed to be the same as that of light, till something appears to the contrary. An ordinary fire, red hot charcoal, or indeed any heated body, radiates heat, which is capable of being reflected to a focus, like the light and heat of the sun; but it should seem to be not of sufficient energy to penetrate glass, or other transparent bodies so as to be refracted to an efficient focus.

Several new and important facts relative to the radiation of heat, have lately been ascertained by Professor Leslie, and published in his "Inquiry on Heat." Having invented an ingenious and delicate air thermometer, well adapted for the purpose, he was enabled to mark the effects of radiation in a great variety of cases and circumstances, with more precision than had previously been done. Some of the principal facts respecting the radiation of heat, which have either been discovered or confirmed by him, it will be proper to mention.

1. If a given vessel be filled with hot water, the quantity of heat which radiates from it, depends chiefly upon the nature of the exterior surface of the vessel. Thus, if a canister of tinned iron be the vessel, then a certain quantity of heat radiates from it; if the said vessel be covered with black paint, paper, glass, etc. it will then radiate 8 times as much heat in like circumstances.

2. If the bulb of the thermometer be covered with tinfoil, the impression of the radiant heat is only $1/_5$th of that upon the glass surface.

3. A metallic mirror reflects 10 times as much heat from an ordinary fire, or from any heated body, as a similar

glass mirror does. This last is found to reflect the heat from its *anterior* surface, and not from the quicksilvered one, which is the most essential in reflecting solar light and heat. Here then is a striking difference between solar and culinary heat.

From these facts it appears, that metals and other bodies which are eminently disposed to *reflect* radiant heat, are not disposed to *absorb* it in any remarkable degree; whereas, black paint, paper, glass, etc. are disposed to *absorb* it, and consequently to *radiate* it again in proper circumstances.

4. Screens of glass, paper, tinfoil, etc. being placed between the radiating body and the reflector, were proved to intercept the radiant heat completely; but being heated themselves by the direct radiant heat, in time the thermometer was affected by their radiation. The heat radiating from hot water, does not then seem capable of being transmitted through glass, like the solar heat.

5. Radiant heat suffers no sensible loss in its passage through the air; a greater or less radiant body produces the same effect, provided it subtends the same angle at the reflector, agreeing with light in this respect.

6. The intensity of reflected heat diminishes inversely as the distance; whereas, in light, it is the same at all distances; the focus of heat too differs from that of light; it is nearer the reflector; the heating effect diminishes rapidly in going outwards, but slowly in going inwards towards the reflector. This seems to intimate the want of perfect elasticity in radiant heat.

7. A hollow globe of tin, four inches in diameter, being filled with hot water, cooled from 35° to 25° centi-

grade in 156 minutes; the same painted with lamp-black, cooled from 35° to 25° in 81 minutes. The air of the room was 15°.

8. When a heated body is whirled through the air, the additional cooling effect is directly proportional to the velocity.

9. In air the rate of cooling of a hollow glass globe filled with hot water, and that of the same globe covered with tinfoil, is not constant at all temperatures. The disproportion is greater in low termperatures, and less in high. Thus, in the present case, Mr. Leslie finds the variable ratio to be as 105 + h for glass, and as 50 + h for tin, where h represents the elevation of temperature in degrees. According to this the rate of cooling of a vitreous and a metallic surface is nearly the same at very high temperatures; but is nearly as 105 to 50, when h is very little. No differences are observed in their rates of cooling in water.

10. After a long and intricate, but ingenious investigation, Mr. Leslie finds the cooling power of the air upon a hollow sphere, six inches in diameter, and filled with boiling water, to be as follows: namely, in each minute of time the fluid loses the following fractional parts of its excess of temperature, by the three distinct sources of refrigeration in the air undermentioned:

By abduction, that is, the proper conducting power of air, the 524th.

By recession, that is, the perpendicular current of air excited by the heated body, the h × 21715th.

By pulsation, or radiation, the 2533d part from a metalic surface, and eight times as much, or the 317th part from a surface of paper; (It should be observed, that Mr.

Leslie contends that air is instrumental in the radiation of heat, which is contrary to the received opinion.)

11. A body cools more slowly in rarefied air, than in air of the common density: and the different species of air have their respective refrigerating powers. Common air and hydrogenous gas exhibit remarkable differences. According to Mr. Leslie, if the cooling power of common air upon a vitreous surface be denoted by unity, that of hydrogenous gas will be denoted by 2.2857; and upon a metallic surface the ratio is .5 to 1.7857. In common air the loss from a vitreous surface is .57 by radiation, and .43 by the other two causes: from a metallic surface, .07 and .43. In hydrogenous gas the loss from a vitreous surface is .57 by radiation, and 1.71 by the other causes; from a metallic surface, .07 and 1.71. He finds the radiation to be the same in the two gases, and to be very little diminished by rarefaction; but the effects of the other refrigerating powers rapidly diminish with the density.

Those who wish to see the experiments and reasonings from which these important conclusions are derived, must have recourse to Mr. Leslie's work: but as some of the facts and opinions appear from my experience to be questionable, I shall now proceed to state what has occurred to me on these subjects. I have no reason to withhold my assent from the first 8 articles; but the last 3 are not equally satisfactory.

Before we enter upon a detail of experiments, it will be proper to point out the correspondence of the new thermometric scale with the old one in the higher parts, it being only given briefly in the table, page 11.

Correspondences of the Thermometric Scales.

old scale.	new scale.	old scale.	new scale.
212°	212°	409.8°	342°
225	222	427.3	352
238.6	232	445.3	362
252.6	242	463.6	372
266.8	252	482.2	382
281.2	262	501	392
296.2	272	520.3	402
311.5	282	539.7	412
327	292	559.8	422
342.7	302	580.1	432
359.2	312	600.7	442
375.8	322	621.6	452
392.7	332	642	462

Experiment 1.

A mercurial thermometer having a bulb of half an inch in diameter, and a scale of about 8 inches long from freezing to boiling mercury, was heated to 442° new scale, and suffered to cool in a horizontal position in air of 42°. The bulb in this and every other instrument projected several inches below the scale. The times of cooling were the same from 442° to 242°, from 242° to 142°, and from 142° to 92°, namely, 2 minutes and 20 seconds each. This was often repeated; the times of cooling were always within 4 or 5 seconds of that above, and when any differences in the successive intervals took place, the times were always observed to be rather less in the higher, and more in the lower parts of the scale.

From this experiment it appears, that the thermometer was raised 400° above the temperature of the air, or to 600° of the old scale; it lost 200° of temperature in the first interval of time, 100° in the second, and 50° in the third. This result goes to establish the principle announced at page 9, that, according to the new graduation, *the temperature descends in geometrical progression to equal increments of time.*

Experiment 2.

According to Mr. Leslie, the same law of cooling does not take place from a metallic as from a vitreous surface; this always appeared to me very surprising, and I was anxious to satisfy myself more particularly as to the fact. With this view, I took another mercurial thermometer, with a bulb of .7 inch diameter, and scale of 12 inches, having a range from 0 to 300° old scale, and corresponding new scale attached to it. This was heated, and the times of cooling through every successive 10 degrees of the new scale were noticed repeatedly; the bulb was then covered with tinfoil, pasted upon it, and the surface made as smooth as well could be; the thermometer was then heated, and the times of cooling were again noticed as before, repeatedly. The mean results follow; and a column of the differences of the logarithms of the degrees expressing the elevation of temperature above that of the surrounding air, which was 40°. The temperature of the thermometer was raised to 275° per scale; that is, 235° above the air, and it is obviously most convenient to reckon from the temperature of the air considered as zero: in which case 19 represents the difference of the logarithms of 235 and 225, etc.

Thermom. cooled.			Bulb clear. Seconds.	Bulb coated with tinfoil. Seconds.	Dif. of Logarith.
From	235°	to 225°	in 11	17	19
	225	to 215	12	18	20
	215	to 205	13	18	21
	205	to 195	14	19	22
	195	to 185	15	20	23
	185	to 175	16	22	24
	175	to 165	17	24	25
	165	to 155	19	26	27
	155	to 145	20	28	29
	145	to 135	21	30	31
	135	to 125	22	31	33
	125	to 115	24	33	36
	115	to 105	27	36	39
	105	to 95	30	40	43
	95	to 85	34	48	48
	85	to 75	39	54	54
	75	to 65	45	62	62
	65	to 55	52	73	73
	55	to 45	62	88	87
	45	to 35	78	110	109
	35	to 25	120	165	146
	25	to 15	160	244	222
			851	1206	1193

By inspecting this table, it appears that the whole time of cooling when the bulb was clear was 851 seconds, and when covered with tinfoil was 1206 seconds, which numbers are nearly as 17 to 24. But the times in cooling from 175° to 165° were 17 and 24 seconds respectively; and the times in cooling from 95° to 85° were 34 and 48 respectively, which are exactly in the ratio of the whole times: and by examining any two corresponding times, they will be found to be as 17 to 24 nearly. Whence it follows that the same law of progressive cooling applies to a metallic as to a vitreous surface, contrary to the results of Mr. Leslie's experience. It must not however be understood that this ratio for the two kinds of surfaces is quite correct; however carefully the bulb of a thermometer may be coated with tinfoil, the surface is necessarily enlarged, which makes it cool more quickly than if the metallic surface were the very same quantity as the vitreous.

The differences of the logarithms happening accidentally so nearly to coincide in magnitude with the times of cooling of the metallic surface, they require no reduction, and we have an opportunity of seeing how far the law of geometrical progression in cooling is supported by this experiment. It appears that for 5 or 6 of the highest intervals of temperature, the times of cooling were rather smaller, and for the two last rather larger than required by the law.

Experiment 3.

As Mr. Leslie found the times of cooling of metallic surfaces considerably enlarged, in moderate elevations of temperature more especially, I took another thermometer having a smaller bulb, and a scale of an inch for 10 degrees, this was treated as in the last experiment, and the results were as under:

Thermom. cooled.					Bulb clear. seconds.	Bulb coated with tinfoil. seconds.	Log. ratios. reduced.
From	75°	to	65°	in	38	46	46
	65	to	55		46	55	54
	55	to	45		54	64	65
	45	to	35		65	78	81
	35	to	25		86	103	109
	25	to	15		130	158	165
	15	to	5		310	370	355
					729	874	875

Here the whole times of cooling, and the several parts are almost accurately as 10 for the vitreous, and as 12 for the metallic surface. They very nearly accord too with the logarithmic ratios. The effect of the metallic surface differs less from that of the vitreous in this than in the former experiment; because the bulb being smaller, it was more than proportionally increased in surface by the tinfoil, which was pasted on in small slips, and consequently was twofold in many places.

Being from these results pretty well satisfied that the surfaces of bodies do not disturb the law of their refrigeration, though they materially affect the time, yet in consequence of the general accuracy of Mr. Leslie's experiments, I was desirous to ascertain the results in his own way, more particularly because for the reason assigned above, my method did not give the true rates of cooling of *equal* surfaces.

Experiment 4.

I took two new tin canisters, such as are commonly used for tea, of a cylindrico-conical shape, and each capable of holding 15 oz. of water. The surface of one of them was covered with brown paper pasted on it; instead of the usual lid, a cork of $1^{1}/_{2}$ inch. diameter was adapted to both, and through a hole in the center of this, the tube of a delicate thermometer was inserted, with a scale of the new graduation affixed above the cork. Both canisters were contrived to be suspended by small strings when filled with water, and to have the thermometer with its bulb in their centers. They were successively filled with boiling water, and suspended in the middle of a room of the temperature 40°, and the times of cooling through each successive 10 degrees were noticed as below.

Water cooled.			Canister covered with paper.	Naked canister.	Logarith. ratios.
From 205°	to	195°	in 6.5 min.	10 min.	11
195	to	185	7	10.5	12
185	to	175	7.5	11+	13
175	to	165	8+	12	13
165	to	155	9	13.5	14
155	to	145	10	15	16
145	to	135	11.5	17	17
135	to	125	13	19	19
125	to	115	14.5	21.5	22
115	to	105	16	24	25
105	to	95	20	30	29
95	to	85	25	38	35
85	to	75	31	46	44
75	to	65	40	60	60
			219	327.5	330

Here the results are equally satisfactory and important; not only the times of cooling are in the uniform ratio of 2 to 3 throughout the range; but they almost exactly accord with the logarithmic ratios, indicating the geometric progression in cooling. As experiments of this sort are capable of being repeated by anyone without the aid of any expensive instrument or any extraordinary dexterity; it will be unnecessary to insist upon the accuracy of the above. It will be understood that the range of cooling was from 205° of the new scale, to 65° of the same, the air being 40°, or 25° below the extremity of the range, which corresponds with 57° of the old scale.

It will be proper now to inquire into the cause of the difference in the times of cooling arising from the variation of surface. Mr. Leslie has shown the surface has no influence upon the time of cooling when immersed in water; it should seem then that the difference of surfaces in the expenditure of heat arises from their different powers of radiation solely; indeed Leslie has proved by direct experiments that the heat radiating from a vitreous or paper surface is 8 times as great as that from a metallic surface. Taking this for granted, we can easily find the portions of heat dispersed by radiation, and conducted away by the atmosphere. For, let 1 denote the quantity of heat conducted away by the atmosphere, from a vitreous or metallic surface in any given small portion of time, and x the quantity radiated from a metallic surface in the same time; then $8x$ will be the quantity radiated from a vitreous surface in that time; and from the result of the last experiment we shall have, $2:3::1+x:1+8x$; whence $2+16x=3+3x$, and $x=^{1}/_{13}$; this gives $1^{1}/_{13}$, for the whole heat discharged by metal, and $1^{8}/_{13}$ for that discharged by glass in the same time, where the unit expresses the part conducted, and the fraction the part radiated.

That is, from a metallic surface 13 parts of heat are conducted away by the air and 1 part radiated; from a vitreous surface 13 parts are conducted, and 8 parts radiated, in a given time.

The quantity of heat discharged by radiation from the most favorable surface, therefore, is probably not more than .4 of the whole and that conducted away by the air not less than .6. Mr. Leslie however deduces .57 for the former, and .43 for the latter; because he found the disproportion in the times of cooling of vitreous and metallic surfaces greater than I find it in the lower part of the scale.

The obvious consequences of this doctrine in a practical sense are,

1. In every case where heat is required to be retained as long as possible, the containing vessel should be of metal, with a bright clear surface.

2. Whenever heat is required to be given out by a body with as much celerity as possible, the containing vessel, if of metal, ought to be painted, covered with paper, charcoal, or some animal or vegetable matter; in which case the heat given out will be 3 parts for 2 from a metallic surface.

Refrigeration of Bodies in various Kinds of Elastic Fluids.

Bodies cool in very different times in some of the elastic fluids. Mr. Leslie was the first, I believe, who noticed this fact; and he has given us the results of his experiments on common air and hydrogenous gas, of the common density, and also rarefied in various degrees. I made some experiments with a view to determine the relative cooling powers of the gases, the results of which it may be proper to give. My apparatus was a strong phial, containing about 15 or 20 cubic inches; a perforated cork containing the stem of a thermometer was adapted to it, so as to be air tight; two marks were made with a file on the tube of the thermometer, comprising an interval of 15 or 20°, about blood heat. The bottle was filled with any proposed gas, and after it had acquired the temperature of the surrounding air, the stopper was withdrawn, and the heated thermometer with its cork was instantly inserted; the number of seconds which elapsed whilst the mercury descended from the upper to the under mark were then noted, as under. The surrounding air was of a constant temperature.

Thermometer immersed In carbonic acid gas	cooled in 112 seconds.
—sulphuretted hydrogen, nitrous oxide, and olefiant gas	100+
—com. air, azotic and oxyg. gas	100
—nitrous gas	90
—carburet. hyd. or coal gas	70
—hydrogen	40

The refrigerating effect of hydrogen is truly remarkable; I cooled the thermometer 10 times successively in a bottle of hydrogen gas; at each experiment the instrument was taken out, and the stopper put in, till the original temperature was restored; by this, a portion of the hydrogen escaped each time, and an equal portion of common air was admitted; the times of cooling regularly increased as follows; viz. 40, 43, 46, 48, 51, 53, 56, 58, 60 and 62 seconds, respectively; at this time the mixture was examined, and found half hydrogen and half common air. Equal measures of hydrogen and common air were then mixed together, and put into the bottle, and the heated thermometer was found to cool from mark to mark, in 62 seconds as before.

Condensed air cools bodies more rapidly than air of common density; and rarefied air less rapidly, whatever be the kind. The results of my own experience for common air were as follows:

Density of the air.	Therm. cools in
2	85 seconds.
1	100
$1/2$	116
$1/4$	128
$1/8$	140
$1/16$	160
$1/32$	170

A small receiver of hydrogen gas, which cooled the thermometer in 40 seconds, when rarefied 7 or 8 times, took 70 seconds to cool the same. But the exact effects of rarefaction on this and the other gases were not determined.

From Mr. Leslie, we learn that in hydrogenous gas, there is little difference between the time of cooling of a vitreous and metallic surface, the former being as 2.28, and the latter as 1.78, from which he justly infers "this inequality of effect [between atmospheric air and hydrogenous gas] proves its influence to be exerted chiefly, if not entirely, in augmenting the abductive portion."

The expenditure of heat by radiation being the same in hydrogenous gas as in atmospheric air, we may infer it is the same in every other species of gas; and therefore is performed independently of the gas, and is carried on the same in vacuo as in air. Indeed Mr. Leslie himself admits that the diminution of the effect consequent upon rarefaction is extremely small, which can scarcely be conceived if air were the medium of radiation.

The effect of radiation being allowed constant, that of the density of the air may be investigated, and will be found, I believe, to vary nearly or accurately as the cube root of the density. In order to compare this hypothesis with observation, let 100 = time of cooling in atmospheric air, the density being 1; then from what has been said above, .4 will represent the heat lost by a vitreous surface by radiation, and .6 that lost by the conducting power of the medium. Let t = the time of cooling in air of the density d; then if $100 : .4 :: t : .004$ t = the heat lost by radiation; but the heat conducted away is, by hypothesis, as the time $\times$ by the cube root of the density = .006 $t\sqrt[3]{d}$; whence $.004t + .006t\sqrt[3]{d} = 1$, and

$$t = \frac{1}{.004 + .006\sqrt[3]{d}}$$

Calculating from this formula, we shall find the times of cooling in common air of the several densities as under:

Density of the air.	Times of cooling.
2	86.5 seconds.
1	100
$1/2$	114
$1/4$	129
$1/8$	143
$1/16$	157
$1/32$	170
$1/64$	182
$1/128$	193
$1/$infinity.	250

This table accords nearly with the preceding one, the result of actual observation. In the same way might the times of cooling of a metallic surface in rarefied air be found, by substituting .0007 for .004, and .0093 for .006 in the preceding formula.

The cooling power of hydrogenous gas independent of radiation, may be found thus: if $100'' : .4 :: 40'' : .16 =$ the heat lost by radiation in that gas in 40 seconds; whence $.84 =$ the heat conducted away by the air in $40''$, or .021 per second; but in common air the loss per second by abduction is only .006; from this it appears that the refrigerating power of hydrogenous gas is $3^1/_2$ times as great as that of common air.

It may be asked what is the cause why different gases have such different cooling effects, especially on the supposition of each atom of all the different species possessing the same quantity of heat? To this we may answer that the gases differ from each other in two essential points, in the number of atoms in a given volume, and in the weight or inertia of their respective atoms. Now both number and weight tend to retard the motion of a current: that is, if two gases possess the same number of particles in a given volume, it is evident that one will disperse heat most quickly which has its atoms of the least weight; and if other two gases have particles of the same weight, that one will most disperse heat which has the least number in a given volume; because the resistance will be as the number of particles to be moved, in like circumstances. Of the gases that have nearly the same number of particles in the same volume, are, hydrogen, carburetted hydrogen, sulphuretted hydrogen, nitrous oxide, and carbonic acid. These conduct heat in the order they are written, hydrogen best and carbonic acid worst; and the weights of their ultimate particles increase in the same order (see page 58). Of those that have their atoms of the same weight and their number in a given volume different, are oxygen and carburetted hydrogen: the latter has the greater cooling power and the fewer particles in a given volume.

On the Temperature of the Atmosphere

It is a remarkable fact, and has never, I believe, been satisfactorily accounted for, that the atmosphere in all places and seasons is found to decrease in temperature in proportion as we ascend, and nearly in an arithmetical progression. Sometimes the fact may have been otherwise, namely, that the air was colder at the surface of the earth than above, particularly at the breaking of a frost, I have observed it so; but this is evidently the effect of great and extraordinary commotion in the atmosphere, and is at most of a very short duration. What then is the occasion of this diminution of temperature in ascending? Before this question can be solved, it may be proper to consider the defects of the common solution. Air, it is said, is not heated by the direct rays of the sun; which pass through it as a transparent medium, without producing any calorific effect, till they arrive at the surface of the earth. The earth being heated, communicates a portion to the contiguous atmosphere, whilst the superior strata in proportion as they are more remote, receive less heat, forming a gradation of temperature, similar to what takes place along a bar of iron when one of its ends is heated.

The first part of the above solution is probably correct: Air, it should seem, is singular in regard to heat; it neither receives nor discharges it in a radiant state; if so, the propagation of heat through air must be effected by its conducting power, the same as in water. Now we know that heat applied to the under surface of a column of water is propagated upwards with great celerity, by the actual ascent of the heated particles: it is equally certain too that heated air ascends. From these observations it should follow that the causes assigned above for the gradual change of temperature in a perpendicular column of the atmosphere, would apply directly to a state of temperature the very reverse of the fact; namely, to one in which the higher the ascent or the more remote from the earth the higher should be the temperature.

Whether this reasoning be correct or not, it must I think be universally allowed, that the fact has not hitherto received a satisfactory explanation. I conceive it to be one involving a new principle of heat; by which I mean a principle that no other phenomenon of nature presents us with, and which is not at present recognized as such. I shall endeavor in what follows to make out this position.

The principle is this: *The natural equilibrium of heat in an atmosphere, is when each atom of air in the same perpendicular column is possessed of the same quantity of heat;* and consequently, *the natural equilibrium of heat in an atmosphere is when the temperature gradually diminishes in ascending.*

That this is a just consequence cannot be denied,

when we consider that air increases in its capacity for heat by rarefaction: when the quantity of heat is given or limited, therefore the temperature must be regulated by the density.

It is an established principle that any body on the surface of the earth unequally heated is observed constantly to tend towards an equality of temperature; the new principle announced above, seems to suggest an exception to this law. But if it be examined, it can scarcely appear in that light. *Equality of heat and equality of temperature,* when applied to the same body in the same state, are found so uniformly to be associated together, that we scarcely think of making any distinction between the two expressions. No one would object to the commonly observed law being expressed in these terms: *When any body is unequally heated, the equilibrium is found to be restored when each particle of the body becomes in possession of the same quantity of heat.* Now the law thus expressed is what I apprehend to be the true general law, which applies to the atmosphere as well as to other bodies. It is an *equality of heat,* and not *an equality of temperature* that nature tends to restore.

The atmosphere indeed presents a striking peculiarity to us in regard to heat: we see in a perpendicular column of air, a body without any change of form, slowly and gradually changing its capacity for heat from a less to a greater; but all other bodies retain a uniform capacity throughout their substance.

If it be asked why an equilibrium of heat should turn upon the equality in *quantity* rather than in *temperature;* I answer that I do not know: but I rest the proof of it upon the fact of the inequality of temperature observed in ascending into the atmosphere. If the natural tendency of the atmosphere was to an equality of temperature, there does not appear to me any reason why the superior regions of the air should not be at least as warm as the inferior.

The arguments already advanced on behalf of the principle we are endeavoring to establish, are powerfully corroborated by the following facts: By the observations of Bouguer, Saussure, and Gay Lussac, we find that the temperature of the air at an elevation where its weight is $1/2$ that at the surface, is about 50° Fahrenheit less than that at the surface: and from my experiments (Manch. Mem. vol. 5. page 525.) it appears that air being suddenly rarefied from 2 to 1 produces 50° of cold. Whence we may infer, that a measure of air at the earth's surface being taken up to the height above-mentioned, preserving its original temperature, and suffered to expand, would become two measures, and be reduced to the same temperature as the surrounding air; or *vice versa,* if two measures of air at the proposed height were condensed into one measure, their temperature would be raised 50°, and they would become the same in density and temperature, as the like volume of air at the earth's surface. In like manner we may infer, that if a volume of air from the earth's surface, to the summit of the atmosphere were condensed and brought into a horizontal position on the earth's surface, it would become of the same density and temperature as the air around it, without receiving or parting with any heat whatever.

Another important argument in favor of the theory here proposed may be derived from the contemplation of an atmosphere of vapor. Suppose the present aerial atmosphere were to be annihilated, and one of steam or aqueous vapor were substituted in its place; and suppose further, that the temperature of this atmosphere at the earth's surface were everywhere 212° and its weight equal to 30 inches of mercury. Now at the elevation of about 6 miles the weight would be 15 inches or $1/2$ of that below, at 12 miles, it would be 7.5 inches, or $1/4$ of that at the suface, etc. and the temperature would probably diminish 25° at each of those intervals. It could not diminish more; for we have seen (page 11) that a diminution of temperature of 25° reduces the force of vapor one half; if therefore a greater reduction of temperature were to take place, the weight of the incumbent atmosphere would condense a portion of the vapor into water, and the general equilibrium would thus be disturbed perpetually from condensations in the upper regions. But if we suppose on the other hand, that the diminution of temperature in each of these intervals is less than 25°, then the upper regions could admit of more vapor without condensation; but it must take place at the surface, because vapor at 212° cannot sustain more than the weight of 30 inches of mercury.

These three supposed cases of an aqueous vapor atmosphere may be otherwise stated thus:

1. The specific gravity of steam at the earth's surface being supposed .6 of atmospheric air, and the weight of the atmosphere of steam equal to 30 inches of mercury, its temperature at the surface would be 212°; at 6 miles high, 187°; at 12 miles, 162°; at 18 miles, 137°; at 24 miles, 112°, etc.—In this case the density, not only at the surface, but everywhere, would be a maximum, or the greatest possible for the existing temperature; so that a perfect equilibrium having once obtained, there could be neither condensation nor evaporation in any region. For every 400 yards of elevation, the thermometer would descend 1 degree.

2. If the atomosphere were constituted just as above, except that the temperature now diminished more rapidly

than at the rate of 25° for 6 miles; then the temperature of the higher regions not being sufficient to support the weight, a condensation must take place; the weight would thus be diminished, but as the temperature at the surface is always supposed to be kept at 212°, evaporation must go on there with the design to keep up the pressure at 30 inches. Thus there would be perpetual strife between the recently raised vapor ascending, and the condensed drops of rain descending. A position much less likely than the preceding one.

3. The same things being supposed as before, but now the temperature decreases more slowly than at the rate of 25° for 6 miles: in this case the density of the steam at the earth's surface would be a maximum for the temperature, but nowhere else; so that if a quantity of water were taken up to any elevation it would evaporate; but the increased weight of the atmosphere would produce a condensation of steam into water on the ground. In this case then there would not be that equilibrium, which we see in the 1st case, and which accords so much more with the regularity and simplicity generally observable in the laws of nature.*

* I owe to Mr. Ewart the first hint of the idea respecting elastic fluids, which I have endeavored to expand in the present section; he suggested to me some time ago, that it was probable steam of any low temperature, as 32°, of maximum density, contained the same quantity of absolute heat as the like weight of steam of 212° of maximum density; and that consequently if it could be gradually compressed without losing any heat, that is, if the containing vessel kept pace with it in increase of temperature, there would never be any condensation of steam into water, but it would constantly retain its elasticity.

In fact the heat (1000°), which is given out by steam when it is condensed into water, is merely heat of compression; there is no change in the affinity of the molecules of water for heat; the expulsion is occasioned solely by the approximation of the molecules, and would be precisely the same whether that approximation was occasioned by external compression or internal attraction. Indeed if we estimate the temperature that would be given out by the mechanical compression of steam from a volume of 2048 to that of 1, by successively doubling the density, and supposing as above, that at each time of doubling, 25' were given out, it would be found that 12 successive operations would reduce the volume to 1, and that only 300° would be given out. But it is not right to conclude, that the same quantity of temperature would be given out at each of the successive condensations, though it may be nearly so for most of them: towards the conclusion, the space occupied by the solid atom or particle bears a considerable proportion to the whole space occupied by it and its atmosphere. At the first compression, the atmosphere of heat might be said to be reduced into half the space; but at the last, the reduction would be much greater, and therefore more heat given out than determined by theory.

Since writing the above, Mr. Ewart informs me that the idea respecting steam, which I had from him, is originally Mr. Watt's. In Black's Lectures, Vol. 1, page 190, the author, speaking of Mr. Watt's experiments on steam at low temperatures, observes, "we find that the latent heat of the steam is at least as much increased as the sensible heat is diminished." It is wonderful that so remarkable a fact should have been so long known and so little noticed.

That an atmosphere of steam does actually surround the earth, existing independently of the other atmospheres with which however it is necessarily most intimately mixed, is I think capable of demonstration. I have endeavored to enforce and illustrate it in several Essays in the Memoirs of the Manchester Society, and in Nicholson's Journal, to which I must refer. Now an atmosphere of any elastic fluid, whether of the weight of 30 inches of mercury, or of half an inch, must observe the same general laws; but is should seem that an atmosphere of vapor varies its temperature less rapidly in ascending than the one we have of air. Something of an effect similar to what is pointed out in the 2d case above, ought therefore to be observed in our mixed atmosphere; namely, a condensation of vapor in the higher regions, at the same moment that evaporation is going on below. This is actually the case almost every day, as all know from their own observation; a cloudy stratum of air frequently exists above, while the region below is comparatively dry.

Section 9

On the Phenomena of the Congelation

of Water

Several remarkable phenomena are attendant upon the congelation of water, and some of them are so different from what might be expected from analogy, that I believe no explanation according with the principles of the mechanical philosophy has been attempted, such as to account for all the appearances. This attempt is the object of the present Essay. It will be expedient previously to state the principal facts.

1. The specific gravity of ice is less than that of water in the ratio of 92 to 100.

2. When water is exposed in a large suspended jar to cool in still air of 20 or 30°, it may be cooled 2 or 3° below freezing; but if any tremulous motion take place, there appear instantly a multitude of shining hexangular *spiculae*, floating, and slowly ascending in the water.

3. It is observed that the shoots or ramifications of ice at the commencement, and in the early stage of congelation are always at an angle of 60 or 120°.

4. Heat is given out during congelation, as much as

would raise the temperature of water 150° of the new scale. The same quantity is again taken in when the ice is melted. This quantity may be $1/_{40}$ of the whole heat which water of 32° contains.

5. Water is densest at 36° of the old scale, or 38° of the new: from that point it gradually *expands* by cooling or by heating alike, according to the law so often mentioned, that of the square of the temperature.

6. If water be exposed to the air, and to agitation, it cannot be cooled below 32°; the application of cold freezes a part of the water, and the mixture of ice and water requires the temperature of 32°.

7. If the water be kept still, and the cold be not severe, it may be cooled in large quantities to 25° or below, without freezing; if the water be confined in the bulb of a thermometer, it is very difficult to freeze it by any cold mixture above 15° of the old scale; but it is equally difficult to cool the water much below that temperature without its freezing. I have obtained it as low as 7 or 8°, and gradually heated it again without any part of it being frozen.

8. In the last case of what may be called *forced* cooling, the law of expansion is still observed as given above.

9. When water is cooled to 15° or below in a bulb, it retains the most perfect transparency; but if it accidentally freeze, the congelation is instantaneous, the bulb becoming in a moment opaque and white like snow, and the water is projected up the stem.

10. When water is cooled below freezing, and congelation suddenly takes place, the temperature rises instantly to 32°.

In order to explain these phenomena, let it be conceived that the ultimate or smallest elements of water are
all globular, and exactly of the same size; let the arrangement of these atoms be in squares, as exhibited in Fig. 1.
Plate 3. so that each particle touches four others in the
same horizontal plane. Conceive a second stratum of particles placed upon these in like order of squares, but so that
each globule falls into the concavity of four others on the
first stratum, and consequently rests upon four points,
elevated 45° above the centers of the globules. A perpendicular section of such globule resting upon two diagonal
globules of the square is exhibited in Fig. 3. Conceive a
third stratum placed in like manner upon the second, etc.
The whole being similar to a square pile of shot. The
above constitution is conceived to represent that of water
at the temperature of greatest density.

To find the number of globules in a cubic vessel, the
side of which is given; let n = the number of particles in
one line or side of the cube; then n^2 is the number in any
horizontal stratum; and because a line joining the centers
of two contiguous particles in different strata makes an
angle of 45° with the horizontal plane, the number of
strata in the given height will be $n \div$ sine of 45° = $n = \frac{1}{2}$
$\sqrt{2}$. Whence the number of particles in the cubic vessel
= $n^3 \div \frac{1}{2}\sqrt{2} = n^3\sqrt{2}$.

Now let it be supposed that the square pile is instantly
drawn into the shape of a rhombus (Fig. 2.); then each
horizontal stratum will still consist of the same number of
particles as before, only in a more condensed form, each
particle being now in contact with six others. But to
counteract this condensation, the several successive strata
are more elevated than before, so that the pile is increased
in height. A question then arises whether a vessel of given
capacity will hold a greater number of particles in this or

the former disposition? It must be observed, that in the last case, each particle of a superior stratum rests only on two particles of an inferior one, and is therefore elevated by the sine of 60° as represented in Fig. 4. The bases of the two piles are as 1 : $\sqrt{3/4}$, and their heights as $\sqrt{1/2}$: $\sqrt{3/4}$ but the capacities are as the products of the base and height, or as $\sqrt{1/2}$: $3/4$ that is, as .707 to .750 nearly, or as 94 to 100. Thus it appears that the first arrangement contains more particles in a given space than the second by 6 per cent.

The last or rhomboidal arrangement is supposed to be that which the particles of water assume upon congelation. The specific gravities of ice and water should therefore be as 94 to 100. But it should be remembered that water usually contains 2 per cent. in bulk of atmosphere air: and that this air is liberated upon congelation; and is commonly entangled amongst the ice in such sort as to increase its bulk without materially increasing its weight; this reduces the specific gravity of ice 2 per cent. or makes it 92, which agrees exactly with observation. Hence the 1st fact is explained.

The angle of a rhombus is 60°, and its supplement 120°; if any particular angles are manifested in the act of congelation, therefore we ought to expect these, agreeable to the 2d and 3d phenomena.

Whenever any remarkable change in the internal constitution of any body takes place, whether by the accession and junction of new particles, or by new arrangements of those already existing in it; some modification in the atmospheres of heat must evidently be required; though it may be difficult to estimate the quantity, and sometimes even the kind of change so produced, as in the present case. So far therefore the theory proposed agrees with the 4th phenomenon.

In order to explain the other phenomena, it will be requisite to consider more particularly the mode by which bodies are expanded by heat. Is the expansion occasioned simply by the enlargement of the individual atmospheres of the component particles? This is the case with elastic fluids, and perhaps with solids, but certainly not with liquids. How is it possible that water should be expanded a portion represented by 1 upon the addition of a certain quantity of heat at one temperature, and by 340 upon the addition of a like quantity at another temperature, when both temperatures are remote from the absolute zero, the one perhaps 6000° and the other 6170°? The fact cannot be accounted for on any other supposition than that of a change of arrangement in the component particles; and a *gradual* change from the square to the rhomboidal arrangement is in all probability effected both by the addition and abstraction of heat. It is to be supposed then that water of the greatest possible density has its particles arranged in the square form; but if a given quantity of heat be added to, or taken from it, the particles commence their approach to the rhomboidal form, and consequently the whole is expanded, and that the same by the same change of temperature, whether above or below that point.

If heat be taken away from water of 38°, then expansion is the consequence, and a moderate inclination of the particles towards the rhomboidal form; but this only extends a small way whilst the mass is subject to a tremulous motion, so as to relieve the obstructions occasioned by friction; by the energy of certain affinities, the new form is completed in moment, and a portion of ice formed; heat is then given out which retards the subsequent formation, till at last the whole is congealed. This is the ordinary process of congelation. But if the mass of water cooled is kept in a state of perfect tranquility, the gradual approach to the rhomboidal form can be carried much farther; the expansion goes on according to the usual manner, and the slight friction or adhesion of the particles is sufficient to counteract the balance of energies in favor of the new formation, till some accidental tremor contributes to adjust the equilibrium. A similar operation is performed when we lay a piece of iron on a table, and hold a magnet gradually nearer and nearer; the proximity of the approach, without contact, is much assisted by guarding against any tremulous motion of the table. Hence the rest of the phenomena are accounted for.

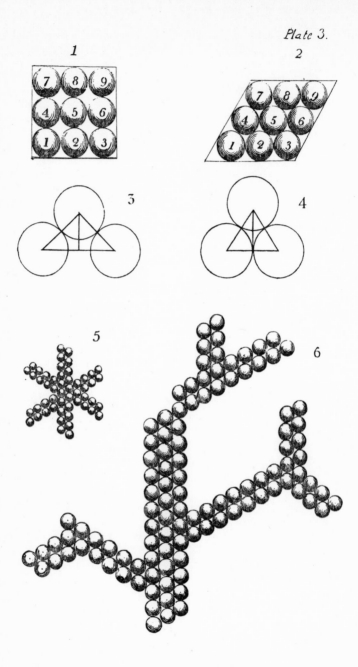

Plate 3.

PLATE III. (See Chapter I, Section 9, on Congelation of Water.)
—The balls in Fig. 1 and 2 represent particles of water: in the former, the square form denotes the arrangement in water, the rhombodial form in the latter, denotes the arrangement in ice. The angle is always 60° or 120°.

Fig. 3. represents the perpendicular section of a ball resting upon two others, as 4 and 8, Fig. 1.

Fig. 4. represents the perpendicular section of a ball resting upon two balls, as 7 and 5, Fig. 2. The perpendiculars of the triangles show the heights of the strata in the two arrangements.

Fig. 5. represents one of the small spiculae of ice formed upon the sudden congelation of water cooled below the freezing point.

Fig. 6. represents the shoots or ramifications of ice at the commencement of congelation. The angles are 60° and 120°.

CHAPTER II

ON THE CONSTITUTION

OF BODIES

There are three distinctions in the kinds of bodies, or three states, which have more especially claimed the attention of philosophical chemists; namely, those which are marked by the terms *elastic fluids, liquids, and solids*. A very familiar instance is exhibited to us in water, of a body, which, in certain circumstances, is capable of assuming all the three states. In steam we recognise a perfectly elastic fluid, in water, a perfect liquid, and in ice a complete solid. These observations have tacitly led to the conclusion which seems universally adopted, that all bodies of sensible magnitude, whether liquid or solid, are constituted of a vast number of extremely small particles, or atoms of matter bound together by a force of attraction, which is more or less powerful according to circumstances, and which as it endeavors to prevent their separation, is very properly called in that view, *attraction of cohesion*; but as it collects them from a dispersed state (as from steam into water) it is called, *attraction of aggregation,* or more simply, *affinity*. Whatever names it may go by, they still signify one and the same power. It is not my design to call in question this conclusion, which appears completely satisfactory; but to show that we have hitherto made no use of it, and that the consequence of the neglect, has been a very obscure view of chemical agency, which is daily growing more so in proportion to the new lights attempted to be thrown upon it.

The opinions I more particularly allude to, are those of Berthollet on the Laws of chemical affinity; such as that chemical agency is proportional to the mass, and that in all chemical unions, there exist insensible gradations in the proportions of the constituent principles. The inconsistence of these opinions, both with reason and observation, cannot, I think, fail to strike every one who takes a proper view of the phenomena.

Whether the ultimate particles of a body, such as water, are all alike, that is, of the same figure, weight, etc. is a question of some importance. From what is known, we have no reason to apprehend a diversity in these particulars: if it does exist in water, it must equally exist in the elements constituting water, namely, hydrogen and oxygen. Now it is scarcely possible to conceive how the aggregates of dissimilar particles should be so uniformly the same. If some of the particles of water were heavier than others, if a parcel of the liquid on any occasion were constituted principally of these heavier particles, it must be supposed to affect the specific gravity of the mass, a circumstance not known. Similar observations may be made on other substances. Therefore we may conclude that *the ultimate particles of all homogeneous bodies are perfectly alike in weight, figure, etc.* In other words, every particle of water is like every other particle of water; every particle of hydrogen is like every other particle of hydrogen, etc.

Besides the force of attraction, which, in one character or another, belongs universally to ponderable bodies, we find another force that is likewise universal, or acts upon all matter which comes under our cognizance, namely, a force of repulsion. This is now generally, and I think properly, ascribed to the agency of heat. An atmosphere of this subtile fluid constantly surrounds the atoms of all bodies, and prevents them from being drawn into actual contact. This appears to be satisfactorily proved by the observation, that the bulk of a body may be diminished by abstracting some of its heat: But from what has been stated in the last section, it should seem that enlargement and diminution of bulk depend perhaps more on the arrangement, than on the size of the ultimate particles. Be this as it may, we cannot avoid inferring from the preceding doctrine on heat, and particularly from the section on the natural zero of temperature, that solid bodies, such as ice, contain a large portion, perhaps $4/5$ of the heat which the same are found to contain in an elastic state, as steam.

We are now to consider how these two great antagonist powers of attraction and repulsion are adjusted, so as to allow of the three different states of *elastic fluids, liquids, and solids.* We shall divide the subject into four Sections; namely, first, *on the constitution of pure elastic fluids;* second, *on the constitution of mixed elastic fluids;* third, *on the constitution of liquids,* and fourth, *on the constitution of solids.*

Section 1

On the Constitution of Pure Elastic Fluids

A pure elastic fluid is one, the constituent particles of which are all alike, or in no way distinguishable.
Steam, or aqueous vapor, hydrogenous gas, oxygenous gas,
azotic gas,* and several others are of this kind. These fluids
are constituted of particles possessing very diffuse atmospheres of heat, the capacity or bulk of the atmosphere
being often one or two thousand times that of the particle
in a liquid or solid form. Whatever therefore may be the
shape or figure of the solid atom abstractedly, when surrounded by such an atmosphere it must be globular; but as
all the globules in any small given volume are subject to
the same pressure, they must be equal in bulk, and will
therefore be arranged in horizontal strata, like a pile of
shot. A volume of elastic fluid is found to expand whenever the pressure is taken off. This proves that the repul-

* The novice will all along understand that several chemical subjects
are necessarily introduced before their general history and character can
be discussed.

sion exceeds the attraction in such case. The absolute attraction and repulsion of the particles of an elastic fluid, we have no means of estimating, though we can have little doubt but that the cotemporary energy of both is great; but the excess of the repulsive energy above the attractive can be estimated, and the law of increase and diminution be ascertained in many cases. Thus in steam, the density may be taken at $^1/_{1728}$ that of water; consequently each particle of steam has 12 times the diameter that one of water has, and must press upon 144 particles of a watery surface; but the pressure upon each is equivalent to that of a column of water of 34 feet; therefore the excess of the elastic force in a particle of steam is equal to the weight of a column of particles of water, whose height is $34 \times 144 = 4896$ feet: And further, this elastic force decreases as the distance of the particles increases. With respect to steam and other elastic fluids then, the force of cohesion is entirely counteracted by that of repulsion, and the only force which is efficacious to move the particles is the excess of the repulsion above the attraction. Thus, if the attraction be as 10 and the repulsion as 12, the effective repulsive force is as 2. It appears then, that an elastic fluid, so far from requiring any force to separate its particles, always requires a force to retain them in their situation, or to prevent their separation.

A vessel full of any pure elastic fluid presents to the imagination a picture like one full of small shot. The globules are all of the same size; but the particles of the fluid differ from those of the shot, in that they are constituted of an exceedingly small central atom of solid matter, which is surrounded by an atmosphere of heat, of great density next to the atom, but gradually growing rarer according to some power of the distance; whereas those of the shot are globules, uniformly hard throughout, and surrounded with atmospheres of heat of no comparative magnitude.

It is known from experience, that the force of a mass of elastic fluid is directly as the density. Whence is derived the law already mentioned, that the repulsive power of each particle is inversely as its diameter. That is, the *apparent* repulsive power, if we may so speak; for the real or absolute force of repulsion is not known, as long as we remain ignorant of the attractive force. When we expand any volume of elastic fluid, its particles are enlarged, without any material change in the quantity of their heat; it follows then, that the density of the atmospheres of heat must fluctuate with the pressure. Thus, suppose a measure of air were expanded into 8 measures; then, because the diameters of the elastic particles are as the cube root of the space, the distances of the particles would be twice as great as before, and the elastic atmospheres would occupy nearly 8 times the space they did before, with nearly the same quantity of heat: whence we see that these atmospheres must be diminished in density in nearly the same ratio as the mass of elastic fluid.

Some elastic fluids, as hydrogen, oxygen, etc. resist any pressure that has yet been applied to them. In such then it is evident the repulsive force of heat is more than a match for the affinity of the particles, and the external pressure united. To what extent this would continue we cannot say; but from analogy we might apprehend that a still greater pressure would succeed in giving the attractive force the superiority, when the elastic fluid would become a liquid or solid. In other elastic fluids, as steam, upon the application of compression to a certain degree, the elasticity apparently ceases altogether, and the particles collect in small drops of liquid, and fall down. This phenomenon requires explanation.

From the very abrupt transition of steam from a volume of 1700 to that of 1, without any material increase of pressure, one would be inclined to think that the condensation of it was owing to the *breaking* of a spring, rather than to the *curbing* of one. The last however I believe is the fact. The condensation arises from the action of affinity becoming superior to that of heat, by which the latter is overruled, but not weakened. As the approximation of the particles takes place, their repulsion increases from the condensation of the heat, but their affinity increases, it should seem, in a still greater ratio, till the approximation has attained a certain degree, when an equilibrium between those two powers takes place, and the liquid, water, is the result. That this is the true explanation we may learn from what has been stated at page 102; wherein it is shown that the heat given off by the condensation of steam, is in all probability no more than would be given off by any permanently elastic fluid, could it be mechanically condensed into the like volume, and is moreover a small portion of the whole heat previously in combination. As far then as the heat is concerned in this phenomenon, the circumstances would be the same whether the approximation of the particles was the effect of affinity, or of external mechanical force.

The constitution of a liquid, as water, must then be conceived to be that of an aggregate of particles, exercising in a most powerful manner the forces of attraction and repulsion, but nearly in an equal degree. Of this more in the sequel.

Section 2

On the Constitution of Mixed Elastic Fluids

When two or more elastic fluids, whose particles do not unite chemically upon mixture, are brought together, one measure of each, they occupy the space of two measures, but become uniformly diffused through each other, and remain so, whatever may be their specific gravities. The fact admits of no doubt; but explanations have been given in various ways, and none of them completely satisfactory. As the subject is one of primary importance in forming a system of chemical principles, we must enter somewhat more fully into the discussion.

Dr. Priestley was one of the earliest to notice the fact: it naturally struck him with surprise, that two elastic fluids, having apparently no affinity for each other, should not arrange themselves according to their specific gravities, as liquids do in like circumstances. Though he found this was not the case after the elastic fluids had once been thoroughly mixed, yet he suggests it as probable, that if two of such fluids could be exposed to each other without agitation, the one specifically heavier would retain its lower situation. He does not so much as hint at such gases being retained in a mixed state by affinity. With regard to his suggestion of two gases being carefully exposed to each other without agitation, I made a series of experiments expressly to determine the question, the results of which are given in the Manch. Memoirs, Vol. 1. *new series*. From these it seems to be decided that gases always intermingle and gradually diffuse themselves amongst each other, if exposed ever so caerfully; but it requires a considerable time to produce a complete intermixture, when the surface of communication is small. This time may vary from a minute, to a day or more, according to the quantity of the gases and the freedom of communication.

When or by whom the notion of mixed gases being held together by chemical affinity was first propagated, I do not know; but it seems probable that the notion of water being dissolved in air, led to that of air being dissolved in air. Philosophers found that water gradually disappeared or evaporated in air, and increased its elasticity; but steam at a low temperature was known to be unable to overcome the resistance of the air, therefore the agency of affinity was necessary to account for the effect. In the permanently elastic fluids indeed, this agency did not seem to be so much wanted, as they are all able to support themselves; but the diffusion through each other was a circumstance which did not admit of an easy solution any other way. In regard to the solution of water in air, it was natural to suppose, nay, one might almost have been satisfied without the aid of experiment, that the different gases would have had different affinities for water, and that the quantities of water dissolved in like circumstances, would have varied according to the nature of the gas. Saussure found however that there was no difference in this respect in the solvent powers of carbonic acid, hydrogen gas, and common air. It might be expected that at least the *density* of the gas would have some influence upon its solvent powers, that air of half density would take half the water, or the quantity of water would diminish in some proportion to the density; but even here again we are disappointed; whatever be the rarefaction, if water be present, the vapor produces the same elasticity, and the hygrometer finally settles at extreme moisture, as in air of common density in like circumstances. These facts are sufficient to create extreme difficulty in the conception how any principle of affinity or *cohesion* between air and water can be the agent. It is truly astonishing that the same quantity of vapor should cohere to *one* particle of air in a given space, as to *one thousand* in the same space. But the wonder does not cease here; a Torricellian vacuum dissolves water; and in this instance we have vapor existing independently of air at all temperatures; what makes it still more remarkable is, the vapor in such vacuum is precisely the same in quantity and force as in the like volume of any kind of air of extreme moisture.

These and other considerations which occurred to me some years ago, were sufficient to make me altogether abandon the hypothesis of air dissolving water, and to explain the phenomena some other way, or to acknowledge they were inexplicable. In the autumn of 1801, I hit upon an idea which seemed to be exactly calculated to explain the phenomena of vapor; it gave rise to a great variety of experiments upon which a series of essays were founded, which were read before the Literary and Philosophical Society of Manchester, and published in the 5th Vol. of their memoirs, 1802.

The distinguishing feature of the new theory was, that

the particles of one gas are not elastic or repulsive in regard to the particles of another gas, but only to the particles of their own kind. Consequently when a vessel
contains a mixture of two such elastic fluids, each acts
independently upon the vessel, with its proper elasticity,
just as if the other were absent, while no mutual action
between the fluids themselves is observed. This position
most effectually provided for the existence of vapor of any
temperature in the atmosphere, because it could have
nothing but its own weight to support; and it was perfectly
obvious why neither more nor less vapor could exist in air
of extreme moisture, than in a vacuum of the same temperature. So far then the great object of the theory was
attained. The law of the condensation of vapor in the atmosphere by cold, was evidently the same on this scheme,
as that of the condensation of pure steam, and experience
was found to confirm the conclusion at all temperatures.
The only thing now wanting to completely establish the
independent existence of aqueous vapor in the atmosphere, was the conformity of other liquids to water, in
regard to the diffusion and condensation of their vapor.
This was found to take place in several liquids, and particularly in sulphuric ether, one which was most likely to
show any anomaly to advantage if it existed, on account of
the great change of expansibility in its vapor at ordinary
temperatures. The existence of vapor in the atmosphere
and its occasional condensation were thus accounted for;
but another question remained, how does it rise from a
surface of water subject to the pressure of the atmosphere?
The consideration of this made no part of the essays above-
mentioned, it being apprehended, that if the other two
points could be obtained by any theory, this third too,
would, in the sequel, be accomplished.

From the novelty, both in the theory and the experiments, and their importance, provided they were correct, the essays were soon circulated, both at home and abroad. The new facts and experiments were highly valued, some of the latter were repeated, and found correct, and none of the results, as far as I know, have been contraverted; but the theory was almost universally misunderstood, and consequently reprobated. This must have arisen partly at least from my being too concise, and not sufficiently clear in its exposition.

Dr. Thomson was the first, as far as I know, who publicly animadverted upon the theory; this gentleman, so well known for his excellent System of Chemistry, observed in the first edition of that work, that the theory would not account for the equal distribution of gases; but that, granting the supposition of one gas neither attracting nor repelling another, the two must still arrange themselves according to their specific gravity. But the most general objection to it was quite of a different kind; it was admitted, that the theory was adapted so as to obtain the most uniform and permanent diffusion of gases; but it was urged, that as one gas was as a vacuum to another, a measure of any gas being put to a measure of another, the two measures ought to occupy the space of one measure only. Finding that my views on the subject were thus misapprehended, I wrote an illustration of the theory, which was published in, the 3d Vol. of Nicholson's Journal, for November, 1802. In that paper I endeavored to point out the conditions of mixed gases more at large, according to my hypothesis; and particularly touched upon the discriminating feature of it, that of two particles of any gas A, repelling each other by the known stated law, while one or more particles of another gas B; were interposed in a direct line, without at all affecting the reciprocal action of the said two particles of A. Or, if any particles of B were casually to come in contact with one of A, and press against it, this pressure did not preclude the cotemporary action of all the surrounding particles of A upon the one in contact with B. In this respect the mutual action of particles of the same gas was represented as resembling magnetic action, which is not disturbed by the intervention of a body not magnetic.

As the subject has since received the animadversions of several authors, which it is expedient to notice more or less, it will be proper to point out the order intended to be pursued. First, I shall consider the objections to the new theory made by the several authors, with their own views on the subject; and then shall give what modifications of the theory, the experience and reflection of succeeding time have suggested to me. The authors are Berthollet, Dr. Thomson, Mr. Murray, Dr. Henry, and Mr. Gough.

Berthollet in his Chemical Statics (1804) has given a chapter on the constitution of the atmosphere, in which he has entered largely into a discussion of the new theory. This celebrated chemist, upon comparing the results of experiments made by De Luc, Saussure, Volta, Lavoisier, Watt, etc. together with those of Gay Lussac, and his own, gives his full assent to the fact, that vapors of every kind increase the elasticity of each species of gas alike, and just as much as the force of the said vapors in vacuo; and not only so, but that the specific gravity of vapor in air and vapor in vacuo is in all cases the same (Vol. 1. Sect. 4.) Consequently he adopts the theorem for finding the quantity of vapor which a given volume of air can dissolve, which I have laid down; namely,

$$s = \frac{p}{p-f}$$

where p represents the pressure upon a given volume (1) of dry air, expressed in inches of mercury, $f =$ the force of the vapor in vacuo at the temperature, in inches of mercury, and $s =$ the space which the mixture of air and vapor occupies under the given pressure, p, after saturation. So far therefore we perfectly agree: but he objects to the theory by which I attempt to explain these phenomena, and substitutes another of his own.

The first objection I shall notice is one that clearly shows Berthollet either does not understand, or does not rightly apply the theory he opposes; he says, "If one gas occupied the interstices of another, as though they were vacancies, there would not be any augmentation of volume when aqueous or ethereal vapor was combined with the air; nevertheless there is one proportional to the quantity of vapor added: humidity should increase the specific gravity of the air, whereas it renders it specifically lighter, as has been already noticed by Newton." This is the objection which has been so frequently urged; it has even been stated by Mr. Gough, if I understand him aright, in almost the same words (Nicholson's Journal, Vol. 9, page 162); yet this last gentleman is profoundly skilled in the mechanical action of fluids. Let a tall cylindrical glass vessel containing dry air be inverted over mercury, and a portion of the air drawn out by a syphon, till an equilibrium of pressure is established within and without; let a small portion of water, ether, etc. be then thrown up into the vessel; the vapor rises and occupies the interstices of the air as a void; but what is the obvious consequence? Why, the surface of the mercury being now pressed both by the dry air, and by the new raised vapor, is more pressed within than without, and an enlargement of the volume of air is unavoidable, in order to restore the equilibrium. Again, in the open air: suppose there were no aqueous atmosphere

around the earth, only an azotic one = 23 inches of mercury, and an oxygenous one = 6 inches. The air being
thus perfectly dry, evaporation would commence with
great speed. The vapor first formed being constantly urged
to ascend by that below, and as constantly resisted by the
air, must, in the first instance, dilate the other two atmospheres; (for, the ascending steam adds its force to the
upward elasticity of the two gases, and in part alleviates
their pressure, the necessary consequence of which is
dilatation.) At last when all the vapor has ascended, that
the temperature will admit of, the aqueous atmosphere
attains an equilibrium; it no longer presses upon the other
two, but upon the earth; the others return to their original
density and pressure throughout. In this case it is true,
there would not be any augmentation of volume when
aqueous vapor was combined with the air; humidity would
increase the weight of the congregated atmospheres, but
diminish their specific gravity under a given pressure. One
would have thought that this solution of the phenomenon
upon my hypothesis was too obvious to escape the notice of
any one in any degree conversant with pneumatic chemistry. Berthollet indeed inquires, "Is such a division of the
same pressure of the atmosphere analogous with any physical property yet known? Can it be conceived that an elastic
substance exists, which adds its volume to that of another,
and which nevertheless does not act on it by its expansive
force?" Certainly; we can not only conceive it, but bring
an instance that must be allowed to be in point. Two
magnets repel each other, that is, act upon each other with
an expansive force, yet they do not act upon other bodies
in the same way, but merely as inelastic bodies; and this no
doubt would be the same if they were reduced to atoms: So
two particles of the same kind of air may act upon each

other elastically, and upon other bodies inelastically, and therefore not at all, unless when in contact.

Berthollet observes, "Hydrogen gas and oxygen gas form water in a given circumstance; azotic gas, and oxygen gas, can also produce nitric acid; but the reciprocal action which decides the combinations cannot be considered as a force commencing at the precise moment at which it is manifested, it must have existed long before producing its effect, and increases gradually till it becomes preponderant." It is no doubt true that the opposite powers of attraction and repulsion are frequently, perhaps constantly, energetic at the same instant; but the effect produced in those cases arises from the difference of the two powers. When the excess of the repulsive power above the attractive in different gases is comparatively small and insignificant, it constitutes that character which may be denominated neutral, and which I supposed to exist in the class of mixed gases which are not observed to manifest any sign of chemical union. I would not be understood to deny an energetic affinity between oxygen and hydrogen, etc. in a mixed state; but that affinity is more than counterbalanced by the repulsion of the heat, except in circumstances which it is not necessary at present to consider.

Again, "Azotic gas comports itself with oxygen gas, in the changes occasioned by temperature and pressure, precisely like one and the same gas: Is it necessary to have recourse to a supposition which obliges us to admit so great a difference of action without an ostensible cause?" It is possible this may appear an objection to a person who does not understand the theory, but it never can be any to one who does. If a mixture of gas, such as atmospheric air, containing azote pressing with a force equal to 24 inches of mercury, and oxygen with a force equal to 6 inches, were suddenly condensed into half the compass, the azotic gas would then evidently, on my hypothesis, press with a force = 48 inches, and the oxygen with a force = 12 inches, making together 60 inches, just the same as any simple gas. And a similar change in the elasticity of each would take place by heat and cold. Will the opposite theory of Berthollet be equally free from this objection? We shall presently examine it.

Another objection is derived from the very considerable time requisite for a body of hydrogen to descend into one of carbonic acid; if one gas were as a vacuum for another, why is the equilibrium not instantly established? This objection is certainly plausible; we shall consider it more at large hereafter.

In speaking of the pressure of the atmosphere retaining water in a liquid state, which I deny, Berthollet adopts the idea of Lavoisier, "that without it the moleculae would be infinitely dispersed, and that nothing would limit their separation, unless their own weight should collect them to form an atmosphere." This, I may remark, is not the language dictated by a correct notion on the subject. Suppose our atmosphere were annihilated, and the waters on the surface of the globe were instantly expanded into steam; surely the action of gravity would collect the moleculae into an atmosphere of similar constitution to the one we now possess; but suppose the whole mass of water evaporated amounted in weight to 30 inches of mercury, how could it support its own weight at the common temperature? It would in a short time be condensed into water merely by its weight, leaving a small portion, such as the temperature could support, amounting perhaps to half an inch of mercury in weight, as a permanent atmosphere, which would effectually prevent any more vapor from rising, unless there were an increase of temperature. Does not every one know that water and other liquids can exist in a Torricellian vacuum at low temperatures solely by the pressure of vapor arising from them? What need then of the pressure of the atmosphere in order to prevent an excess of vaporization?

After having concluded that "without the pressure of the aerial atmosphere, liquids would pass to the elastic state," Berthollet proceeds in the very next paragraph to show that the quantity of vapor in the atmosphere may in fact be much *more* than would exist if the atmosphere were suppressed, and hence infers, "that the variations of the barometer occasioned by those of the humidity of the atmosphere may be much greater than was believed by Saussure and De Luc." I cannot see how the author reconciles the opposite conclusions.

The experiments of Fontana on the distillation of water and ether in closed vessels containing air, are adduced to prove, that vapors do not penetrate air with resistance. This is true no doubt; vapor cannot make its way in such circumstances through a long and circuitous route without time, and if the external atmosphere keep the vessel cool, the vapor may be condensed by its sides, and fall down in a liquid form as fast as it is generated, without ever penetrating in any sensible quantity to its remote extremity.

We come now to the consideration of that theory which Berthollet adopts in his explanation of the phenmena of gaseous mixtures. According to his theory, there are two degrees of affinity. The one is strong, makes the particles of bodies approach nearer to each other, and generally expels heat: the effect of this may be called *combination;* for instance, when oxygen gas is put to nitrous gas, the two combine, give out heat, are condensed in volume, and become possessed of properties different from what they had previously. The other is weak; it does not sensibly condense the volume of any mixture, nor give out heat, nor change the properties of the ingredients; its effect may be called *solution* or *dissolution*; for instance, when oxygen gas and azotic gas are mixed in due proportion, they constitute atmospheric air, in which they retain their distinguishing properties.

It is upon this supposed *solution* of one elastic fluid in another that I intend to make a few observations. That I have not misrepresented the author's ideas, will, I think, appear from the following quotations. "When different gases are mixed, whose action is confined to this solution, no change is observed in the temperature, or in the volume resulting from the mixture; hence it may be concluded, that this mutual action of two gases does not produce any condensation, and that it cannot surmount the effort of the elasticity, or the affinity for caloric, so that the properties of each gas are not sensibly changed—." "Although both the solution and combination of two gases are the effect of a chemical action, which only differs in its intensity, a real difference may be established between them, because there is a very material difference between the results: the combination of two gases always leads to a condensation of their volume, and gives rise to new properties; on their solution, the gases share in common the changes arising from compression and temperature, and preserve their individual properties, which are only diminished in the ratio of the slight action which holds them united." (Page 198.) "The mutual affinity of the gases can, therefore, produce between them an effect which is greater than their difference of specific gravity, but which is inferior to the elastic tension which belongs to each molecule of both, so that the volume is not changed by this action; the liquids which take the elastic state, comport themselves afterwards like the gases." (Page 218.) "Solution must be distinguished from combination, not only because in the first, each of the substances is retained by an affinity so weak, that it preserves its dimensions.—" (Page 219.) Again, "It cannot be doubted, that the parts of elastic fluids are *not* endued with the force of cohesion, as the substances dissolved by them undergo an equal distribution, which could not happen but by the means of a reciprocal chemical attraction; that which constitutes the force of cohesion." (Researches into the Laws of chemical affinity, Eng. Trans. page 57.) Here the translator has, I apprehend, mistaken the English idiom. The author means to say, that the parts of elastic fluids *are* endued with the force of cohesion; but this he applies only to heterogeneous particles. He certainly does not mean that the particles of homogeneous elastic fluids possess the force of cohesion.

Newton has demonstrated from the phenomena of condensation and rarefaction that elastic fluids are constituted of particles, which repel one another by forces which increase in proportion as the distance of their centers diminishes: in other words, the forces are reciprocally as the distances. This deduction will stand as long as the Laws of elastic fluids continue to be what they are. What a pity it is that all who attempt to reason, or to theorize respecting the constitution of elastic fluids, should not make themselves thoroughly acquainted with this immutable Law, and constantly hold it in their view whenever they start any new project! When we contemplate a mixture of oxygenous and hydrogenous gas, what does Berthollet conceive, are the particles that repel each other according to the Newtonian Law? The mixture *must* consist of such; and he ought in the very first instance to have informed us what constitutes the *unity* of a particle in his solution. If he grants that each particle of oxygen retains its unity, and each particle of hydrogen does the same, then we must conclude that the mutual action of two particles of oxygen is the same as that of a particle of oxygen, and one of hydrogen, namely, a repulsion according to the Law above stated, which effectually destroys the supposed solution by chemical agency. But if it be supposed that each particle of hydrogen attaches itself to a particle of oxygen, and the two particles so united form *one*, from which the repulsive energy emanates; then the new elastic fluid may perfectly conform to the Newtonian Law; in this case a true saturation will take place when the number of particles of hydrogen and oxygen in a mixture happen to be equal, or at least in the ratio of some simple numbers, such as 1 to 2, 1 to 3, etc. Now something like this does actually take place when a real combination is formed, as for instance, steam, and nitric acid formed of a mixture of oxygen and nitrous gas. Here we have new elastic fluids, the atoms of which repel one another by the common Law, heat is given out, a great condensation of volume ensues, and the new fluids differ from their constituents in their chemical relations. It remains then to determine whether, in the instance of solution, all these effects take place in a "slight" degree; that is, in so small a degree as not to be cognizable to any of the senses. It certainly requires an extraordinary stretch of the imagination to admit the affirmative.

One great reason for the adoption of this, or any other theory on the subject, arises from the phenomena of the evaporation of water. How is water taken up and retained in the atmosphere? It cannot be in the state of vapor, it is said, because the pressure is too great: there must therefore be a true chemical solution. But when we consider that the surface of water is subject to a pressure equal to 30 inches of mercury, and besides this pressure, there is a *sensible* affinity between the particles of water themselves; how does the *insensible* affinity of the atmosphere for water overcome both these powers? It is to me quite inexplicable upon this hypothesis, the leading object of which is to account for this very phenomenon. Further, if a particle of air has attached a particle of water to it, what reason can be assigned why a superior particle of air should rob an inferior one of its property, when each particle possesses the same power? If a portion of common salt be dissolved in water and a little muriatic acid added; is there any reason to suppose the additional acid displaces that already combined with the soda, and that upon evaporation the salt is not obtained with the identical acid it previously had? Or, if oxygen gas be confined by water, is there any reason to suppose that the hydrogen of the water is constantly giving its oxygen to the air and receiving an equal quantity from the same? Perhaps it will be said in the case of air dissolving water, that it is not the affection of one particle for one, it is that of a mass of particles for another mass; it is the united action of all the atoms in the atmosphere upon the water, which raises up a particle. But as all these energies are reciprocal, the water must have a like action on the air, and then an atmosphere over water would press downward by a force greater than its weight, which is contradicted by experience.

When two measures of hydrogen and one of oxygen gas are mixed, and fired by the electric spark, the whole is converted into steam, and if the pressure be great, this steam becomes water. It is most probable then that there is the same number of particles in two measures of hydrogen as in one of oxygen. Suppose then three measures of hydrogen are mixed with one of oxygen, and this slight affinity operates as usual; how is the union effected? According to the principle of equal division, each atom of oxygen ought to have *one atom and a half* of hydrogen attached to it; but this is impossible; one half of the atoms of oxygen must then take two of hydrogen, and the other half, one each. But the former would be specifically lighter than the latter, and ought to be found at the top of the solution; nothing like this is however observed on any occasion.

Much more might be advanced to show the absurdity of this doctrine of the solution of one gas in another, and the insufficiency of it to explain any of the phenomena; indeed I should not have dwelt so long upon it, had I not apprehended that respectable authority was likely to give it credit, more than any arguments in its behalf derived from physical principles.

Dr. Thomson, in the 3d Edition of his System of Chemistry, has entered into a discussion on the subject of mixed gases; he seems to comprehend the excellence and defects of my notions on these subjects, with great acuteness. He does not conclude with Berthollet, that on my hypothesis, "there would not be any augmentation of volume when aqueous and ethereal vapor was combined with the air," which has been so common an objection. There is however one objection which this gentleman urges, that shows he does not completely understand the mechanism of my hypothesis. At page 448, Vol. 3. he observes that from the principles of hydrostatics, "each particle of a fluid sustains the whole pressure. Nor can I perceive any reason why this principle should not hold, even on the supposition that Dalton's hypothesis is well founded." Upon this I would observe, that when once an equilibrium is established in any mixture of gases, each particle of gas is pressed as if by the surrounding particles *of its own kind only*. It is in the renunciation of that hydrostatical principle that the leading feature of the theory consists. The lowest particle of oxygen in the atmosphere sustains the weight of all the particles of oxygen above it, and the weight of no other. It was therefore a maxim with me, that every particle of gas is equally pressed in every direction, but the pressure arises from the particles of its own kind only. Indeed when a measure of oxygen is put to a measure of azote, at the moment the two surfaces come in contact, the particles of each gas press against those of the other with their full force; but the two gases get gradually intermingled, and the force which each particle has to sustain proportionally diminishes, till at last it becomes the same as that of the original gas dilated to twice its volume. The ratio of the forces is as the cube root of the spaces inversely; that is, as $\sqrt[3]{2} : 1$, or as 1.26 : 1 nearly. In such a mixture as has just been mentioned, then, the common hypothesis supposes the pressure of each particle of gas to be 1.26; whereas mine supposes it only to be 1; but the sum of the pressure of both gases on the containing vessel, or any other surface, is exactly the same on both hypotheses.

Excepting the above objection, all the rest which Dr. Thomson has made, are of a nature not so easily to be obviated. He takes notice of the considerable time which elapses before two gases are completely diffused through each other, as Berthollet has done, and conceives this fact, makes against the supposition, that one gas is as a vacuum to another. He further objects, that if the particles of different gases are inelastic to each other; then a particle of oxygen coming into actual contact with one of hydrogen, ought to unite with it, and form a particle of water; but, on the other hand, he properly observes, that the great facility with which such combinations are effected in such instances as a mixture of nitrous and oxygen gas, is an argument in favor of the hypothesis. Dr. Thomson founds another objection upon the facility of certain combina-

tions, when one of the ingredients is in a *nascent* form; that
is, just upon the point of assuming the elastic state; this, he
observes, "seems incompatible with the hypothesis, that
gases are not mutually elastic." Upon the whole, Dr.
Thomson inclines to the opinion of Berthollet, that gases
have the property of dissolving each other; and admits,
"however problematical it may appear at first view, that
the gases not only mutually repel each other, but likewise
mutually attract." I have no doubt if he had taken due
time to consider this conclusion, he would, with me, have
pronounced it absurd: but of this again in the sequel.

With regard to the objection, that one gas makes a
more durable resistance to the entrance of another, than it
ought to do on my hypothesis: This occurred to me in a
very early period of my speculations; I devised the train of
reasoning which appeared to obviate the objection; but it
being necessarily of a mathematical nature, I did not wish
to obtrude it upon the notice of chemical philosophers,
but rather to wait till it was called for. The resistance
which any medium makes to the motion of a body, depends upon the surface of that body, and is greater as the
surface is greater, all other circumstances being the same.
A ball of lead 1 inch in diameter meets with a certain
resistance in falling through the air; but the same ball,
being made into a thousand smaller ones of $1/_{10}$ of an inch
diameter, and falling with the same velocity, meets with 10
times the resistance it did before: because the force of gravity increases as the *cube* of the diameter of any particle,
and the resistance only as the *square* of the diameter.
Hence it appears, that in order to increase the resistance of
particles moving in any medium, it is only necessary to
divide them, and that the resistance will be a maximum
when the division is a maximum. We have only then to
consider particles of lead falling through air by their own

gravity, and we may have an idea of the resistance of one gas entering another, *only the particles of lead must be conceived to be infinitely small,* if I may be allowed the expression. Here we shall find great resistance, and yet no one, I should suppose, will say, that the air and the lead are mutually elastic.

The other two objections of Dr. Thomson, I shall waive the consideration of at present.

Mr. Murray has lately edited a system of chemistry, in which he has given a very clear description of the phenomena of the atmosphere, and of other similar mixtures of elastic fluids. He has ably discussed the different theories that have been proposed on the subject, and given a perspicuous view of mine, which he thinks is ingenious, and calculated to explain several of the phenomena well, but upon the whole, not equally satisfactory with that which he adopts. He does not object to the mechanism of my hypothesis in regard to the independent elasticity of the several gases entering into any mixture, but argues that the phenomena do not require so extraordinary a postulatum; and more particularly disapproves of the application of my theory to account for evaporation.

The principal feature in Mr. Murray's theory, and which he thinks distinguishes it from mine, is "that between mixed gases, which are capable, under any circumstances of combining, an attraction must always be exerted." It is unnceessary to recount the arguments on behalf of this conclusion, because it will not be controverted. Mr. Murray announces his views of the constitution of the atmosphere, as follows: "Perhaps that chemical attraction which subsists between the solid bases of these gases, but which, when they are merely mixed together, cannot, from the distance at which their particles are placed by the repulsive power of caloric, bring them into intimate union, may still be so far exerted, as to prevent their separation: or, they may be retained in mixture by that force of adhesion, which, exerted at the surfaces of many bodies, retains them in contact with considerable force." He supports these notions at length by various observations, and repeats some of the observations of Berthollet, whose doctrine on this subject, as has been seen, is nearly the same.

Before we animadvert on these principles, it may be convenient to extend the first a little farther, and to adopt as a maxim, "that between the particles of *pure* gases, which are capable under any circumstances of combining, an attraction must always be exerted." This, Mr. Murray cannot certainly object to, in the case of steam, a pure elastic fluid, the particles of which are known in certain circumstances to combine. Nor will it be said that steam and a permanent gas are different; for he justly observes, "this distinction (between gases and vapors) is merely relative, and arises from the difference of temperature at which they are formed; the state with regard to each, while they exist in it, is precisely the same." Is steam then constituted of particles in which the attraction is so far exerted as to prevent their separation? No: they exhibit no traces of attraction, more than the like number of particles of oxygen do, when in the gaseous form. What then is the conclusion? It is this: *notwithstanding it must be allowed, that all bodies, at all times, and in every situation, attract one another; yet in certain circumstances, they are likewise actuated by a repulsive power; the only efficient motive force is then the difference of these two powers.*

From the circumstance of gases mixing together without experiencing any sensible diminution of volume, the advocates for the agency of chemical affinity, characterize it as a "slight action," and "a weak reciprocal action:" So far

I think they are consistent; but when we hear of this affinity being so far exerted as to prevent the separation of elastic particles, I do not conceive with what propriety it can be called weak. Suppose this affinity should be exercised in the case of steam of 212°; then the attraction becoming equal to the repulsion, the force which any one particle would exercise must be equal to the weight of a column of water of 4896 feet high. (See page 116.)

It is somewhat remarkable that those gases which are known to combine occasionally, as azote and oxygen, and those which are never known to combine, as hydrogen and carbonic acid, should dissolve one another with equal facility; nay, these last exercise this solvent power with more effect than the former; for, hydrogen can draw up carbonic acid from the bottom to the top of any vessel, notwithstanding the latter is 20 times the specific gravity of the former. One would have thought that a force of adhesion was more to be expected in the particles of steam, than in a mixture of hydrogen and carbonic acid. But it is the business of those who adopt the theory of the mutual solution of gases to explain these difficulties.

In a mixture where are 8 particles of oxygen for 1 of hydrogen, it is demonstrable that the central distances of the particles of hydrogen are at a medium twice as great as those of oxygen. Now supposing the central distance of two adjacent particles of hydrogen to be denoted by 12, query, what is supposed to be the central distance of any one particle of hydrogen from that one particle, or those particles of oxygen with which it is connected by this weak chemical union? It would be well if those who understand and maintain the doctrine of chemical solution would represent how they conceive this to be; it would enable those who are desirous to learn, to obtain a clear idea of the system, and those who are dissatisfied with it, to point out its defects with more precision. The greatest possible central distance would be $8^1/_2$ in the above instance, and the least might perhaps be 1. Berthollet, who decries the diagram by which I endeavored to illustrate my ideas on this subject, has not given us any precise information, either verbally or otherwise, relative to the collocation of the heterogeneous particles, unless it is to be gathered from the consideration that the affinity is so weak that the mixture of fluids preserves its dimensions. What can this weak affinity do, when opposed by a repulsive power of infinite superiority?

In discussing the doctrines of elastic fluids mixed with vapor, Mr. Murray seems disposed to question the accuracy of the fact, that the quantity of vapor is the same in vacuo as in air, though he has not attempted to ascertain in which case it more abounds. This is certainly the touchstone of the mechanical and chemical theories; and I had thought that whoever admitted the truth of the fact, must unavoidably adopt the mechanical theory. Berthollet however, convinced from his own experience, that the fact was incontrovertible, attempts to reconcile it, inimical as it is, to the chemical theory; with what success it is left to others to judge. Mr. Murray joins with Berthollet in condemning as extravagant the position which I maintain, that if the atmosphere were annihilated, we should have little more aqueous vapor than at present exists in it. Upon which I shall only remark, that if either of those gentlemen will calculate, or give a rough estimate upon their hypothesis, of the quantity of aqueous vapor that would be collected around the earth, on the said supposition, I will engage to discuss the subject with them more at large.

In 1802, Dr. Henry announced a very curious and important discovery, which was afterwards published in the Philosophical Transactions; namely, *that the quantity*

*of any gas absorbed by water is increased in direct propor-
tion to the pressure of the gas on the surface of the water.*
Previously to this, I was engaged in an investigation of the
quantity of carbonic acid in the atmosphere; it was matter
of surprise to me that lime water should so readily manifest the presence of carbonic acid in the air, whilst pure
water by exposure for any length of time, gave not the
least traces of that acid. I thought that length of time
ought to compensate for weakness of affinity. In pursuing
the subject I found that the quantity of this acid taken up
by water was greater or less in proportion to its greater or
less density in the gaseous mixture, incumbent upon the
surface, and therefore ceased to be surprised at water ab-
sorbing so insensible a portion from the atmosphere. I had
not however entertained any suspicion that this law was
generally applicable to the gases till Dr. Henry's discovery
was announced. Immediately upon this, it struck me as
essentially necessary in ascertaining the quantity of any gas
which a given volume of water will absorb, that we must
be careful the gas is perfectly pure or unmixed with any
other gas whatever; otherwise the maximum effect for any
given pressure cannot be produced. This thought was suggested to Dr. Henry, and found to be correct; in consequence of which, it became expedient to repeat some of his
experiments relating to the quantity of gas absorbed under
a given pressure. Upon due consideration of all these
phenomena, Dr. Henry became convinced, that there was
no system of elastic fluids which gave so simple, easy and
intelligible a solution of them, as the one I adopt, namely,
that each gas in any mixture exercises a distinct pressure,
which continues the same if the other gases are withdrawn.
In the 8th Vol. of Nicholson's Journal, may be seen a letter
addressed to me, in which Dr. Henry has clearly pointed
out his reasons for giving my theory a preference. In the

9th Vol. is a letter from Mr. Gough, containing some animadversions, which were followed by an appropriate reply from Dr. Henry.

In the 8th, 9th and 10th Volumes of Nicholson's Journal, and in the first Vol. of the Manchester Memoirs (*new series*) may be seen some animadversion of Mr. Gough, on my doctrine of mixed gases, with some of his own opinions on the same subject. Mr. Gough conceives the atmosphere to be a chemical compound of gases, vapor, etc. and he rests his belief chiefly upon the observance of certain hygrometrical phenomena, such as that air absorbs moisture from bodies in certain cases, and in others restores it to them, showing that air has an affinity for water, which may be overcome by another more powerful one. This opinion, as Mr. Murray observes, is the one we have from Dr. Halley; it was supported by Le Roy, Hamilton and Franklin, and might be considered as the prevailing opinion, till Saussure, in his celebrated Essays on hygrometry, published in 1783, suggested that water was first changed into vapor, and was in that state dissolved by the air. This amphibious theory of Saussure does not seem to have gained any converts to it, though it pointed out the instability of the other. Finally, the theory of the chemical solution of water in air, received its death blow in 1791, by the publication of Pictet's Essay on Fire, and more particularly by De Luc's paper on evaporation, published in the Philosophical Transactions for 1792. These gentlemen demonstrated, that all the train of hygrometrical phenomena takes place just as well, indeed rather quicker, in a vacuum, than in air, provided the same quantity of moisture is present. All the influence that any kind or density of air has, is to retard the effect; but in the end it becomes the same.

The only objection which Mr Gough has presented

that appears to me to raise any difficulty, is that in regard
to the propagation of sound: If the atmosphere consist
chiefly of two distinct elastic media, it is urged that distant
sounds ought to be heard double; that is, the same sound
would be heard twice, according as it was brought by one
or other of the atmospheres. By calculation I find that if
sound move at the rate of 1000 feet per second in an atmosphere of azotic gas, it ought to move in the other gases
as follows: namely,

	Feet.	
Sound moves in azotic gas	1000	per second.
——————— oxygen gas	930	————
——————— carb. acid	804	————
——————— aqueous vap.	1175	————

According to this table, if a strong and loud sound
were produced 13 miles off, the first would be a weak impression of it brought by the atmosphere of aqueous vapor,
in 59 seconds; the second would be the strongest of all,
brought by the atmosphere azotic gas, in $68^1/_2$ seconds;
the third would be much inferior to the second, brought
by the oxygenous atmosphere, in 74 seconds; the fourth
and last brought by the carbonic acid atmosphere would be
extremely weak, in 85 seconds. Now though observation
does not perfectly accord with the theory in this respect, it
comes as near it, perhaps, as it does to that of the more
simple constitution of the atmosphere which Mr. Gough
maintains. Derham, who has perhaps made the greatest
number of accurate observations on distant sounds, remarked that the report of a cannon fired at the distance of
13 miles from him, did not strike his ear with a single
sound, but that it was repeated 5 or 6 times close to each
other. "The two first cracks were louder than the third;
but the last cracks were louder than any of the rest."

Cavallo, in his experimental philosophy, after quoting the above observations, proceeds, "this repetition of the sound probably originated from the reflection of a single sound, from hills, houses, or other objects, not much distant from the cannon. But it appears from general observation, and where no echo can be suspected, that the sound of a cannon, at the distance of 10 or 20 miles, is different from the sound when near. In the latter case, the crack is loud and instantaneous, of which we cannot appreciate the height. Whereas in the former case, viz. at a distance, it is a grave sound, which may be compared to a determinate musical sound; and instead of being instantaneous, it begins softly, swells to its greatest loudness, and then dies away growling. Nearly the same thing may be observed with respect to a clap of thunder, other sounds are likewise altered in quality by the distance." (Vol. 2. page 331.)

I shall now proceed to give my present views on the subject of mixed gases, which are somewhat different from what they were when the theory was announced, in consequence of the fresh lights which succeeding experience has diffused. In prosecuting my inquiries into the nature of elastic fluids, I soon perceived it was necessary, if possible, to ascertain whether the atoms or ultimate particles of the different gases are of the same size or volume in like circumstances of temperature and pressure. By the size or volume of an ultimate particle, I mean in this place, the space it occupies in the state of a pure elastic fluid; in this sense the bulk of the particle signifies the bulk of the supposed impenetrable nucleus, together with that of its surrounding repulsive atmosphere of heat. At the time I formed the theory of mixed gases, I had a confused idea, as many have, I suppose, at this time, that the particles of elastic fluids are all of the same size; that a given volume of oxygenous gas contains just as many particles as the same volume of hydrogenous; or if not, that we had no data from which the question could be solved. But from a train of reasoning, similar to that exhibited on page 58, I became convinced that different gases have *not* their particles of the same size: and that the following may be adopted as a maxim, till some reason appears to the contrary: namely,

That every species of pure elastic fluid has its particles globular and all of a size; but that no two species agree in the size of their particles, the pressure and temperature being the same.

There was another thing concerning which I was dubious; whether heat was the cause of repulsion. I was rather inclined to ascribe repulsion to a force resembling magnetism, which acts on one kind of matter, and has no effect on another. For, if heat were the cause of repulsion, there seemed no reason why a particle of oxygen should not repel one of hydrogen with the same force as one of its own kind, especially if they were both of a size. Upon more mature consideration, I see no sufficient reason for discarding the common opinion, which ascribes repulsion to heat; and I think the phenomena of mixed gases may still be accounted for, by repulsion, without the postulatum, that their particles are mutually inelastic, and free from such of the preceding objections as I have left unanswered.

When we contemplate upon the disposition of the globular particles in a volume of pure elastic fluid, we perceive it must be analogous to that of a square pile of shot; the particles must be disposed into horizontal strata, each four particles forming a square: in a superior stratum, each particle rests upon four particles below, the points of its contact with all four being 45° above the horizontal plane, or that plane which passes through the centers of the four particles. On this account the pressure is steady and uniform throughout. But when a measure of one gas is presented to a measure of another in any vessel, we have then a surface of elastic globular particles of one size in contact with an equal surface of particles of another: in such case the points of contact of the heterogeneous particles must vary all the way from 40° to 90°; an intestine motion must arise from this inequality, and the particles of one kind be propelled amongst those of the other. The same cause which prevented the two elastic surfaces from maintaining an equilibrium, will always subsist, the particles of one kind being from the size unable to apply properly to the other, so that no equilibrium can ever take place amongst the heterogeneous particles. The intestine motion must therefore continue till the particles arrive at the opposite surface of the vessel against any point of which they can rest with stability, and the equilibrium at length is acquired when each gas is uniformly diffused through the other. In the open atmosphere no equilibrium can take place in such case till the particles have ascended so far as to be restrained by their own weight; that is, till they constitute a distinct atmosphere.

It is remarkable that when two equal measures of different gases are thus diffused, and sustain an invaried pressure, as that of the atmosphere, the pressure upon each particle after the mixture is less than before. This points out the active principle of diffusion; for, particles of fluids are always disposed to move to that situation where the pressure is least. Thus, in a mixture of equal measures of oxygen and hydrogen, the common pressure on each particle before mixture being denoted by 1, that after the mixture when the gas becomes of half its density, will be denoted by $\sqrt[3]{1/2} = .794$.

This view of the constitution of mixed gases agrees with that which I have given before, in the two following particulars, which I consider as essential to every theory on the subject to give it plausibility.

1st. The diffusion of gases through each other is effected by means of the repulsion belonging to the homogenous particles; or to that principle which is always energetic to produce the dilatation of the gas.

2d. When any two or more mixed gases acquire an equilibrium, the elastic energy of each against the surface of the vessel or of any liquid, is precisely the same as if it were the only gas present occupying the whole space, and all the rest were withdrawn.

In other respects I think the last view accords better with the phenomena, and obviates the objections which Dr. Thomson has brought against the former; particularly in regard to the query, why mixed gases that are known on certain occasions to combine, do not always combine; and why any gaseous particle in its nascent state is more disposed to combination than when it has already assumed the elastic form. It will also more clearly explain the reason of one gas making so powerful and durable a resistance to the entrance of another.

One difficulty still remains respecting vapor, which neither view of the subject altogether removes: though vapor may subsist in the atmosphere upon either supposition, as far as the temperature will admit, not being subject to any more pressure than would arise from its own particles, were the others removed, yet it may be inquired, how does it rise from the surface of water subject to the pressure of the atmosphere? how does vapor which ascends with an elastic force of only half an inch of mercury, detach itself from water when it has the weight of 30 inches of mercury to oppose its ascent? This difficulty applies nearly the same to all theories of the solution of water in air, and it is therefore of consequence for every one, let him adopt what opinion he may, to remove it. Chemical solution but ill explains it; for, the affinity of air for vapor is always described as weak, and yet it is sufficient to overcome the pressure of a powerful force equal to the weight of the atmosphere. I have endeavored to show in another place (Manch. Memoirs, Vol. 1. *new series,* page 284) what my own ideas on the subject are. It appears to me, that it is not till the depth of 10 or 12 strata of particles of any liquid, that the pressure upon each perpendicular column becomes uniform; and that several of the particles in the uppermost stratum are in reality subject to but little pressure.

On the Constitution of Liquids,

And the Mechanical Relations Between Liquids and Elastic Fluids

A liquid or inelastic fluid may be defined to be a body, the parts of which yield to a very small impression, and are easily moved one upon another. This definition may suffice for the consideration of liquids in an hydrostatical sense, but not in a chemical sense. Strictly speaking, there is no substance inelastic; if heat be the cause of elasticity, all bodies containing it must necessarily be elastic: but we commonly apply the word elastic to such fluids only as have the property of condensation in a very conspicuous degree. Water is a liquid or inelastic fluid; but if it is compressed by a great force, it yields a little, and again recovers its original bulk when the pressure is removed. We are indebted to Mr. Canton for a set of experiments by which the compressibility of several liquids is demonstrated. Water, he found, lost about $1/21740$th part of its bulk by the pressure of the atmosphere.

When we consider the origin of water from steam, we have no reason to wonder at its compressibility, and that in a very small degree; it would be wonderful if water had not this quality. The force of steam at 212° is equal to the pressure of the atmosphere; what a prodigious force must it have when condensed 15 or 18 hundred times? We know that the particles of steam, reduced to the state of water, still retain the greatest part of their heat. What a powerful resistance then ought they not to make against a compressing force? The truth is, water, and by analogy, other liquids, must be considered as bodies, under the control of two most powerful and energetic agents, attraction and repulsion, between which there is an equilibrium. If any compressing force is applied, it yields, indeed, but in such a manner, as a strong spring would yield, when wound up almost to the highest pitch. When we attempt to separate one portion of liquid from another, the case is different: here the attraction is the antagonist force, and that being balanced by the repulsion of the heat, a moderate force is capable of producing the separation. But even here we perceive the attractive force to prevail, there being a manifest cohesion of the particles. Whence does this arise? It should seem that when two particles of steam coalesce to form water, they take their station so as to effect a perfect equilibrium between the two opposite powers; but if any foreign force intervene, so as to separate the two molecules an evanescent space, the repulsion decreases faster than the attraction, and consequently this last acquires a superiority or excess, which the foreign force has to overcome. If this were not the case, why do they at first, or upon the formation of water, pass from the greater to the less distance?

With regard to the collocation and arrangement of particles in an aggregate of water or any other liquid, I have already observed (page 108) that this is not, in all probability, the same as in air. It seems highly improbable from the phenomena of the expansion of liquids by heat. The law of expansion is unaccountable for, if we confine liquids to one and the same arrangement of their ultimate particles in all temperatures; for, we cannot avoid concluding, if that were the case, the expansion would go on in a progressive way with the heat, like as in air; and there would be no such thing observed as a point of temperature at which the expansion was stationary.

Reciprocal Pressure of Liquids and Elastic Fluids.

When an elastic fluid is confined by a vessel of certain materials, such as wood, earthenware, etc. it is found slowly to communicate with the external air, to give and receive successively, till a complete intermixture takes place. There is no doubt but this is occasioned by those vessels being porous, so as to transmit the fluids. Other vessels, as those of metal, glass, etc. confine air most completely. These therefore cannot be porous; or rather, their pores are too small to admit of the passage of air. I believe no sort of vessel has yet been found to transmit one gas and confine another; such a one is a desideratum in practical chemistry. All the gases appear to be completely porous, as might be expected, and therefore operate very temporarily in confining each other. How are liquids in this respect? Do they resemble glass, or earthenware, or gases, in regard to their power of confining elastic fluids? Do they treat all gases alike, or do they confine some, and transmit others? These are important questions: they are not to be answered in a moment. We must patiently examine the facts.

Before we can proceed, it will be necessary to lay down a rule, if possible, by which to distinguish the *chemical* from the *mechanical* action of a liquid upon an elastic fluid. I think the following cannot well be objected to: *When an elastic fluid is kept in contact with a liquid, if any change is perceived, either in the elasticity or any other property of the elastic fluid, so far the mutual action must be pronounced* CHEMICAL: *but if* NO *change is perceived, either in the elasticity or any other property of the elastic fluid, then the mutual action of the two must be pronounced wholly* MECHANICAL.

If a quantity of lime be kept in water and agitated, upon standing a sufficient time, the lime falls down, and leaves the water transparent: but the water takes a small portion of the lime which it permanently retains, contrary to the Laws of specific gravity. Why? Because that portion of lime is dissolved by the water. If a quantity of air be put to water and agitated, upon standing a sufficient time, the air rises up to the surface of the water and leaves it transparent; but the water permanently retains a portion of air, contrary to the Laws of specific gravity. Why? Because that small portion of air is dissolved by the water. So far the two explanations are equally satisfactory. But if we place the two portions of water under the receiver of an air pump, and exhaust the incumbent air, the whole portion of air absorbed by the water ascends, and is drawn out of the receiver; whereas the lime remains still in solution as before. If now the question be repeated, why is the air retained in the water? The answer must be, because there is an elastic force on the surface of the water which holds it in. The water appears passive in the business. But, perhaps, the pressure on the surface of the water may have some effect upon its affinity for air, and none on that for lime? Let the air be drawn off from the surfaces of the two portions of water, and another species induced without alleviating the pressure. The lime water remains unchanged; the air escapes from the other much the same as in vacuo.

The question of the relation of water to air appears by this fact to be still more difficult; at first the air seemed to be retained by the attraction of the water; in the second case, the water seemed indifferent; in the third, it appears as if repulsive to the air; yet in all three, it is the same air that has to act on the same water. From these facts, there seems reason then for maintaining three opinions on the subject of the mutual action of air and water; namely, that water attracts air, that water does not attract it, and that water repels air. One of these must be true; but we must not decide hastily. Dr. Priestley once imagined, that the clay of a porous earthen retort, when red hot, "destroys for a time the aerial form of whatever air is exposed to the outside of it; which aerial form it recovers, after it has been transmitted in combination from one part of the clay to another, till it has reached the inside of the retort." But he soon discarded so extravagant an opinion.

From the recent experiments of Dr. Henry, with those of my own, there appears reason to conclude, that a given volume of water absorbs the following parts of its bulk of the several gases.

Bulk of gas absorbed.

1	=	1	Carbonic acid
1	=	2+	Sulphuretted hydrogen
1	=	1−	Nitrous oxide
$\frac{1}{8}$	=	.125	Olefiant gas
$\frac{1}{27}$	=	.037	Oxygenous gas
$\frac{1}{27}$	=	.037	Nitrous gas
$\frac{1}{27}$	=	.037	Carburetted hydrogen
$\frac{1}{27}$	=	.037	Carbonic oxide
$\frac{1}{64}$	=	.0156	Azotic gas
$\frac{1}{64}$	=	.0156	Hydrogenous gas

These fractions are the cubes of $\frac{1}{1}$, $\frac{1}{2}$, $\frac{1}{3}$, $\frac{1}{4}$, etc., this shows the distances of the gaseous particles in the water to be always same multiple of the distances without.

In a mixture of two or more gases, the rule holds the same as when the gases are alone; that is, the quantity of each absorbed is the same as if it was the only gas present.

As the quantity of any gas in a given volume is subject to variation from pressure and temperature, it is natural to inquire whether any change is induced in the absorption of these circumstances; the experiments of Dr. Henry have decided this point, by ascertaining, that if the exterior gas is condensed or rarefied in any degree, the gas absorbed is condensed or rarefied in the same degree; so that the proportions absorbed given above are absolute.

One remarkable fact, which has been hinted at is, that no one gas is capable of retaining another in water; it escapes, not indeed instantly, like as in a vacuum, but gradually, like as carbonic acid escapes into the atmosphere from the bottom of a cavity communicating with it.

It remains now to decide whether the relation between water and the above-mentioned gases is of a chemical or *mechanical* nature. From the facts just stated, it appears evident that the elasticity of carbonic acid and the other two gases of the first class is not at all affected by the water. It remains exactly of the same energy whether the water is present or absent. All the other properties of those gases continue just the same, as far as I know, whether they are alone or blended with water: we must therefore, I conceive, if we abide by the Law just laid down, pronounce the mutual action between these gases and water to be *mechanical*.

A very curious and instructive phenomenon takes place when a portion of any of the above three gases is thrown up into an eudiometer tube of $^3/_{10}$ of an inch diameter over water; the water ascends and absorbs the gas with considerable speed; if a small portion of common air is suddenly thrown up, it ascends to the other, and is commonly separated by a fine film of water for a time. That instant the two airs come into the above situation, the water suddenly ceases to ascent in the tube, but the film of water runs up with great speed, enlarging the space below, and proportionally diminishing that above, till it finally bursts. This seems to show that the film is a kind of sieve through which those gases can easily pass, but not common air.

In the other gases it is very remarkable their density within the water should be such as to require the distance of the particles to be just 2, 3 or 4 times what it is without. In olefiant gas, the distance of the particles within is just twice that without, as is inferred from the density being $1/_8$. In oxygenous gas, etc. the distance is 3 times as great, and in hydrogenous, etc. 4 times. This is certainly curious, and deserves further investigation; but at present we have only to decide whether the general phenomena denote the relation to be of a chemical or mechanical nature. In no case whatever does it appear that the elasticity of any of these gases is affected; if water takes $1/_{27}$ of its bulk of any gas, the gas so absorbed, exerts $1/_{27}$ of the elasticity, that the exterior gas does, and of course it escapes from the water when the pressure is withdrawn from its surface, or when a foreign one is induced, against which it is not a proper match. As far as is known too, all the other properties of the gases continue the same; thus, if water containing oxygenous gas be admitted to nitrous gas, the union of the two gases is certain; after which the water takes up $1/_{27}$ of its bulk of nitrous gas, as it would have done, if this circumstance had not occurred. It seems clear then that the relation is a *mechanical* one.*

* Dr. Thompson and Mr. Murray have both written largely in defense of the notion that *all* gases are combined with water, that a real union by means of a chemical affinity which water exercises in a greater or less degree

Carbonic acid gas then presses upon water in the first instance with its whole force; in a short time it partly enters the water, and then the reaction of the part entered contributes to support the incumbent atmosphere. Finally, the gas gets completely diffused through the water, so as to be of the same density within as without; the gas within

towards all gases, takes place; this affinity is supposed to be of the *slight* kind, or of that kind which holds all gases in a state of solution, one amongst another, without any distinction. The opposite doctrine was first stated in a paper of mine, on the absorption of gases by water. (Manch. Memoirs, *new series,* Vol. 1.) Previously to the publication of that paper, Dr. Henry, who was convinced from his own experience, that the connection of gases with water was of a mechanical nature, wrote two essays in the 8th and 9th Vol. of Nicholson's Journal, in which the arguments for that opinion are clearly, and, I think, unanswerably stated. I do not intend to enter largely into a discussion of the argument these gentlemen adopt. Dr. Thomson's leading argument seems to be, that "water will absorb such a portion of each gas, that the repulsion between the particles absorbed, just balances the affinity of water for them." He then proceeds to infer, that the affinity of carbonic acid for water is such as nearly to balance the elasticity, that the affinity of olefiant gas for water is equal to *half* its elasticity, that of oxygen, $1/_3$, and of azote $1/_4$, etc. Now if a particle of water attract one of carbonic acid by a force analogous to that of repulsion, it must increase directly as the distance decreases; if so, two such particles must be in equilibrium at any distance; and if any other force is applied to the particle of gas propelling it towards the water, the two particles must unite or come into most intimate contact. Hence, I should infer, from Dr. Thomson's principle, that each particle of water would take one of acid, and consequently 1 lb. of water would combine with $2^1/_2$ lbs. of carbonic acid nearly. Mr. Murray mentions a great many circumstances which he conceives make against the mechanical hypothesis; for instance, some of the acid and alkaline gases are known to be absorbed largely by water, and undoubtedly by affinity; therefore the less absorbable gases must be under the same influence, only in an inferior degree, and that "it would be impossible to point out the line of distinction between those where the absorption might be conceived to be purely mechanical, and those where the exertion affinity must be allowed to operate." I conceive nothing is more easy than to point out the exact line of distinction: *wherever water is found to diminish or destroy the elasticity of any gas, it is a chemical agent; wherever it does neither of these, it is a mechanical agent.* Whoever undertakes to maintain the chemical theory of the absorption of gases by water, should in the outset overturn the following argument preferred by Dr. Henry: "The quantity of every gas, absorbed by water, follows exactly the ratio of the pressure; and since it is a rule in philosophising, that effects of the same kind, though differing in degree, are produced by the same cause, it is perfectly safe to conclude, that every, even the minutest portion of any gas, in a state of absorption by water, is retained entirely by incumbent pressure. There is no occasion, therefore, to call in the aid of the law of chemical affinity, when a mechanical law fully and satisfactorily explains the appearances."

the water then presses on the containing vessel only, and reacts upon the incumbent gas. The water then sustains no pressure either from the gas within or without. In olefiant gas the surface of the water supports $7/8$ of the pressure, in oxygenous, etc. $26/27$, and in hydrogenous, etc. $63/64$.

When any gas is confined in a vessel over water in the pneumatic trough, so as to communicate with the atmosphere through the medium of water, that gas must constantly be filtering through the water into the atmosphere, while the atmospheric air is filtering through the water the contrary way, to supply its place in the vessel; so that in due time the air in the vessel becomes atmospheric, as various chemists have experienced. Water in this respect is like an earthenware retort: it admits the gases to go both ways at the same time.

It is not easy to assign a reason why water should be so permeable to carbonic acid, etc. and not to the other gases; and why there should be those differences observable in the others. The densities $1/8$, $1/27$ and $1/64$, have most evidently a reference to a mechanical origin, but none whatever to a chemical one. No mechanical equilibrium could take place if the densities of the gases within were not regulated by this law; but why the gases should not all agree in some one of these forms, I do not see any reason.

Upon the whole it appears that water, like earthenware, is incapable of forming a perfect barrier to any kind of air; but it differs from earthenware in one respect; the last is alike permeable to all the gases, but water is much more permeable to some gases than to others. Other liquids have not been sufficiently examined in this respect.

The mutual action of water, and the greater number of acid gases and alkaline gas partaking most evidently of a chemical nature, will be best considered under the heads of the respective acids and alkalis.

Section 4

On the Constitution of Solids

A solid body is one, the particles of which are in a state of equilibrium betwixt two great powers, attraction and repulsion, but in such a manner, that no change can be made in their distances without considerable force. If an approximation of the particles is attempted by force, then the heat resists it; if a separation, then the attraction resists it. The notion of Boscovich of alternating planes of attraction and repulsion seems unnecessary; except that upon forcibly breaking the cohesion of any body, the newly exposed surface must receive such a modification in its atmosphere of heat, as may prevent the future junction of the parts, without great force.

The essential distinction between liquids and solids, perhaps consists in this, that heat changes the figure of arrangement of the ultimate particles of the former continually and gradually, whilst they retain their liquid form; whereas in the latter, it is probable, that change of temperature does no more than change the size, and not the arrangement of the ultimate particles.

Notwithstanding the *hardness* of solid bodies, or the difficulty of moving the particles one amongst another, there are several that admit of such motion without fracture, by the application of proper force, especially if assisted by heat. The ductility and malleability of the metals, need only to be mentioned. It should seem the particles glide along each others surface, somewhat like a piece of polished iron at the end of a magnet, without being at all weakened in their cohesion. The absolute force of cohesion, which constitutes the *strength* of bodies, is an inquiry of great practical importance. It has been found by experiment, that wires of the several metals beneath, being each $1/10$ of an inch in diameter, were just broken by the annexed weights.

Lead	$29^1/_4$	
Tin	$49^1/_4$	
Copper	$299^1/_4$	
Brass	360	} Pounds.
Silver	370	
Iron	450	
Gold	500	

A piece of good oak, an inch square and a yard long, will just bear in the middle 330 lbs. But such a piece of wood should not in practice be trusted, for any length of time, with above $1/3$ or $1/4$ of that weight. Iron is about 10 times as strong as oak, of the same dimensions.

One would be apt to suppose that *strength* and *hardness* ought to be found proportionate to each other; but this is not the case. Glass is harder than iron, yet the latter is much the stronger of the two.

Crystallization exhibits to us the effects of the natural arrangement of the ultimate particles of various compound bodies; but we are scarcely yet sufficiently acquainted with chemical synthesis and analysis to understand the rationale of this process. The rhomboidal form may arise from the proper position of 4, 6, 8 or 9 globular particles, the cubic form from 8 particles, the triangular form from 3, 6 or 10 particles, the hexahedral prism from 7 particles, etc. Perhaps, in due time, we may be enabled to ascertain the number and order of elementary particles, constituting any given compound element, and from that determine the figure which it will prefer on crystallization, and *vice versa;* but it seems premature to form any theory on this subject, till we have discovered from other principles the number and order of the primary elements which combine to form some of the compound elements of most frequent occurrence; the method for which we shall endeavor to point out in the ensuing chapter.

CHAPTER III

ON CHEMICAL SYNTHESIS

When any body exists in the elastic state, its ultimate particles are separated from each other to a much
greater distance than in any other state; each particle
occupies the center of a comparatively large sphere, and
supports its dignity by keeping all the rest, which by their
gravity, or otherwise are disposed to encroach up it, at a
respectful distance. When we attempt to conceive the
number of particles in an atmosphere, it is somewhat like
attempting to conceive the number of stars in the universe; we are confounded with the thought. But if we limit
the subject, by taking a given volume of any gas, we seem
persuaded that, let the divisions be ever so minute, the
number of particles must be finite; just as in a given space
of the universe, the number of stars and planets cannot be
infinite.

Chemical analysis and synthesis go no farther than to
the separation of particles one from another, and to their

reunion. No new creation or destruction of matter is within the reach of chemical agency. We might as well attempt to introduce a new planet into the solar system, or to annihilate one already in existence; as to create or destroy a particle of hydrogen. All the changes we can produce, consist in separating particles that are in a state of cohesion or combination, and joining those that were previously at a distance.

In all chemical investigations, it has justly been considered an important object to ascertain the relative *weights* of the simples which constitute a compound. But unfortunately the inquiry has terminated here; whereas from the relative weights in the mass, the relative weights of the ultimate particles or atoms of the bodies might have been inferred, from which their number and weight in various other compounds would appear, in order to assist and to guide future investigations, and to correct their results. Now it is one great object of this work, to show the importance and advantage of ascertaining *the relative weights of the ultimate particles, both of simple and compound bodies, the number of simple elementary particles which constitute one compound particle, and the number of less compound particles which enter into the formation of one more compound particle.*

If there are two bodies, A and B, which are disposed to combine, the following is the order in which the combinations may take place, beginning with the most simple:

1 atom of A + 1 atom of B = 1 atom of C, binary.
1 atom of A + 2 atoms of B = 1 atom of D, ternary.
2 atoms of A + 1 atom of B = 1 atom of E, ternary.
1 atom of A + 3 atoms of B = 1 atom of F, quaternary.
3 atoms of A + 1 atom of B = 1 atom of G, quaternary.
etc., etc.

Simple

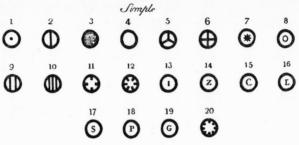

Binary

Ternary

Quaternary

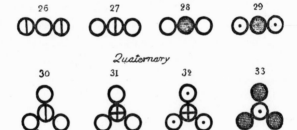

Quinquenary & Sertenary

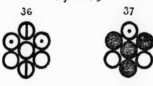

Septenary

PLATE IV. This plate contains the arbitrary marks or signs chosen to represent the several chemical elements or ultimate particles.

Fig.			Fig.		
1	Hydrog.; its rel. weight	1	11	Strontites	46
2	Azote	5	12	Barytes	68
3	Carbon or charcoal	5	13	Iron	38
4	Oxygen	7	14	Zinc	56
5	Phosphorus	9	15	Copper	56
6	Sulphur	13	16	Lead	95
7	Magnesia	20	17	Silver	100
8	Lime	23	18	Platina	100
9	Soda	28	19	Gold	140
10	Potash	42	20	Mercury	167

21. An atom of water or steam, composed of 1 of oxygen and 1 of hydrogen, retained in physical contact by a strong affinity, and supposed to be surrounded by a common atmosphere of heat; its relative weight =   8
22. An atom of ammonia, composed of 1 of azote and 1 of hydrogen   6
23. An atom of nitrous gas, composed of 1 of azote and 1 of oxygen   12
24. An atom of olefiant gas, composed of 1 of carbone and 1 of hydrogen   6
25. An atom of carbonic oxide composed of 1 of carbone and 1 of oxygen   12
26. An atom of nitrous oxide, 2 azote + 1 oxygen   17
27. An atom of nitric acid, 1 azote + 2 oxygen   19
28. An atom of carbonic acid, 1 carbone + 2 oxygen   19
29. An atom of carburetted hydrogen, 1 carbone + 2 hydrogen   7
30. An atom of oxynitric acid, 1 azote + 3 oxygen   26
31. An atom of sulphuric acid, 1 sulphur + 3 oxygen   34
32. An atom of sulphuretted hydrogen, 1 sulphur + 3 hydrogen   16
33. An atom of alcohol, 3 carbone + 1 hydrogen   16
34. An atom of nitrous acid, 1 nitric acid + 1 nitrous gas   31
35. An atom of acetous acid, 2 carbone + 2 water   26
36. An atom of nitrate of ammonia, 1 nitric acid + 1 ammonia + 1 water   33
37. An atom of sugar, 1 alcohol + 1 carbonic acid   35

Enough has been given to show the method; it will be quite unnecessary to devise characters and combinations of them to exhibit to view in this way all the subjects that come under investigation; nor is it necessary to insist upon the accuracy of all these compounds, both in number and weight; the principle will be entered into more particularly hereafter, as far as respects the individual results. It is not to be understood that all those articles marked as simple substances, are necessarily such by the theory; they are only necessarily of such weights. Soda and Potash, such as they are found in combination with acids, are 28 and 42 respectively in weight; but according to Mr. Davy's very important discoveries, they are metallic oxides; the former then must be considered as composed of an atom of metal, 21, and one of oxygen, 7; and the latter, of an atom of metal, 35, and one of oxygen, 7. Or, soda contains 75 per cent. metal and 25 oxygen; potash, 83.3 metal and 16.7 oxygen. It is particularly remarkable, that according to the above-mentioned gentleman's essay on the Decomposition and Composition of the fixed alkalies, in the Philosophical Transactions (a copy of which essay he has just favored me with) it appears that "the largest quantity of oxygen indicated by these experiments was, for potash 17, and for soda, 26 parts in 100, and the smallest 13 and 19."

The following general rules may be adopted as guides in all our investigations respecting chemical synthesis.

1st. When only one combination of two bodies can be obtained, it must be presumed to be a *binary* one, unless some cause appear to the contrary.

2d. When two combinations are observed, they must be presumed to be a *binary* and a *ternary*.

3d. When three combinations are obtained, we may expect one to be a *binary,* and the other two *ternary*.

4th. When four combinations are observed, we should expect one *binary,* two *ternary,* and one *quaternary,* etc.

5th. A *binary* compound should always be specifically heavier than the mere mixture of its two ingredients.

6th. A *ternary* compound should be specifically heavier than the mixture of a binary and a simple, which would, if combined, constitute it; etc.

7th. The above rules and observations equally apply, when two bodies, such as C and D, D and E, etc. are combined.

From the application of these rules, to the chemical facts already well ascertained, we deduce the following conclusions; 1st. That water is a binary compound of hydrogen and oxygen, and the relative weights of the two elementary atoms are as 1 : 7, nearly; 2d. That ammonia is a binary compound of hydrogen and azote, and the relative weights of the two atoms are as 1 : 5, nearly; 3d. That nitrous gas is a binary compound of azote and oxygen, the atoms of which weigh 5 and 7 respectively; that nitric acid is a binary or ternary compound according as it is derived, and consists of one atom of azote and two of oxygen, together weighing 19; that nitrous oxide is a compound similar to nitric acid, and consists of one atom of oxygen and two of azote, weighing 17; that nitrous acid is a binary compound of nitric acid and nitrous gas, weighing 31; that oxynitric acid is a binary compound of nitric acid and oxygen, weighing 26; 4th. That carbonic oxide is a binary compound, consisting of one atom of charcoal, and one of oxygen, together weighing nearly 12; that carbonic acid is a ternary compound, (but sometimes binary) consisting of one atom of charcoal, and two of oxygen, weighing 19; etc., etc. In all these cases the weights are expressed in atoms of hydrogen, each of which is denoted by unity.

From the novelty as well as importance of the ideas suggested in this chapter, it is deemed expedient to give plates, exhibiting the mode of combination in some of the more simple cases.

The elements or atoms of such bodies as are conceived at present to be simple, are denoted by a small circle, with some distinctive mark; and the combinations consist in the juxtaposition of two or more of these; when three or more particles of elastic fluids are combined together in one, it is to be supposed that the particles of the same kind repel each other, and therefore take their stations accordingly.